PATTERNS OF SURVIVAL
AN ANATOMY OF LIFE

BY

JOHN HODGDON BRADLEY

THE EARTH AND ITS HISTORY
PARADE OF THE LIVING
AUTOBIOGRAPHY OF EARTH
FAREWELL THOU BUSY WORLD

PATTERNS
OF SURVIVAL

An Anatomy of Life

By

JOHN HODGDON BRADLEY

GRUNE and STRATTON

1952

First edition published 1938
by the Macmillan Company, New York

Second edition copyright, 1952, by
JOHN HODGDON BRADLEY
Escondido, California

Printed in the U. S. A. for
GRUNE & STRATTON, INC.
381 Fourth Avenue, New York City 16

TO

HAMLIN GARLAND

Acknowledgments

Acknowledgment is gratefully made to the magazines which have published certain sections of this book as articles. Four chapters have appeared essentially in their present form in *The Yale Review.* Two have appeared in abbreviated form in *The American Mercury*, two in *The Forum*, one in *The American Scholar*, and one in *Harper's Magazine.*

Contents

THE QUESTION AND THE QUEST

Men who follow the trails of scientific inquiry are generally more interested in the surface of the world than in its meaning. They are more engaged by the properties of trilobites than of God, more concerned about the exigencies of the Here than the probabilities of the Hereafter. They have learned that Nature vouchsafes no easy victories, that even in her commonest expressions she remains essentially mysterious in the face of their best efforts to understand her. Knowing that answers are usually only new questions in disguise, they tend to avoid the abyss which stretches between science and philosophy.

They tend to avoid it despite the fact that the past half century constitutes perhaps the unhappiest epoch for mysteries in the annals of human thought. With the weapons of observation, measurement, experiment, and induction, science has brought down many a venerable and sturdy enigma, and over the grave of each fallen warrior has inscribed a fitting formula or equation.

Science, indeed, has discovered so many new facts about life and the world it inhabits that information and true enlightenment are apt to be confused. To name a phenomenon, to describe it, perhaps in the end to despise it, is not necessarily to understand it. The lens that discloses a fact but rarely reveals its meaning.

Happily the urge to understand is not all of human desire. Much stronger is the urge to be comfortable. This basic impulse is essentially uniform throughout the living world, whether we call it bluntly the desire of lower creatures to eat, to avoid being eaten, and to reproduce; or more euphemistically regarding ourselves, the desire for life, liberty, and the pursuit of happiness. That science has pleasantly pandered to this urge, no one may honestly deny. We are far better shod than were our grandfathers for the journey from the cradle to the grave. Yet we have hoped, however ungratefully, for more than this.

It is amusing to know that a chair is a tangle of whirling electrons rather than the stolid wood we sit on. It is pleasant to know that should the appendix threaten life, there are surgeons ready to remove it. But it is neither very amusing nor pleasant to realize that many of the men who know most about the living jelly see in it only a mixture of amino-acids, only a busy mart where energy is being acquired from the environment, stored for a time, and then expended. Methods that have bared the inner secrets of tapeworms, bedbugs, and eels have found only a silly myth in the soul of man, and in his body only a degenerating beast.

Ever since the distinguished Liebig nailed to his laboratory door the dictum that "God has ordered all His Creation by Weight and Measure," many biologists have held that all vital activities—from the locomotion of an amoeba to abstract thought—might ultimately be explained wholly in terms of physics and chemistry. But there are others who believe that man at least is something more than mere metabolism. However willing they may be to accept a mechanistic interpretation of the amoeba, they are not willing to accept it for the two-legged creature who is sometimes able to wonder and laugh and dream.

They join the vitalists of old in accusing the mechanists of a fundamental failure. They accuse them of filling libraries with their findings without understanding any better the essential nature of life than did the ancient alchemists who stirred up messes of weird ingredients in the attempt to create a miniature man. And in a sense they are justified. We have today a scarcely more fruitful conception of life than had our ancestors; out of our knowledge of the changes that protein undergoes, we can no better shape a valid conception of their essence or their purpose. Intensive investigation of living creatures has yielded many physical but few philosophical satisfactions.

Yet the vitalists too have failed. To postulate an emotionally satisfactory life principle when life may be known only as a process is at best to make ignorance poetic. The whole long controversy between mechanist and vitalist has been a truly futile business. The essence and purpose of life elude them both. Both are balked by the wall of the same enigma. Below it they stand bewildered and belligerent, wrangling over the name by which it should be known.

Bewilderment, oddly, has stimulated rather than stifled the deep-set desire in the human heart for an emotionally satisfactory cosmogony. Even an occasional scientist, after having been driven for years by curiosity about the relatively unimportant, may begin to yearn for deeper truth. Modern physics has opened the door to a strange new world, exciting beyond anything the mind of man had previously envisaged. Although its revelations are less enlightening than its mysteries are perplexing, it has innocently released a deluge of wild philosophical and theological speculation. Because of what a few scientists have said when wandering beyond their own domain, or because of what their commentators have believed them to have meant to say, almost any giddy assumption may take refuge in a mathematical equation that no one understands. Almost any age-old superstition of the race may be defended in the name of science.

Just possibly the universe might be "mind stuff," or "a

thought in the mind of a Supreme Mathematician," or any of the other things the astro-physicists have called it. It might also just possibly be the essence of jump in the cosmogony of frogs, should frogs be philosophical. It might be these and many other things, and probably is. But to infer from the little that is surely known of it all that the human heart has ever wanted of it is to forsake the proved safeguards against error. The god of modern physics is a bloodless substitute for God the Father and Redeemer. The free will of modern scientific indeterminacy is far from the free will of scholastic philosophy. Evolution with its billion years of waste and torment seems hardly to have been devised with compassion for the sparrows that fall by the way.

Tendency to accept easy and pleasant answers for difficult and disagreeable problems is one of the perennial temptations of man. But there will always be those who are temperamentally barred from the bliss of wishful thinking. Though these reluctant ones may heartily agree with Hamlet that there are more things in Heaven and Earth than are dreamt of in any philosophy, they will yet be unable to accept just any vagrant dream into the sanctuary of verified truth. Aware of the possible existence of supra-sensory truth, they will yet distrust the facile methods which some men use to prove what they want to believe. They will prefer to plod toward truth, however slowly, with the help of observation, measurement, experimentation, and induction, distrustful of wings that might melt away in the sun.

Though rather generally suppressing the temptation to believe in false heavens, science is far from rigidly wedded to the mere collection of facts. It knows that facts are but half of truth, that interpretation is the other half. It seeks and sometimes finds the natural relationships of facts.

These relationships at most are but threads in the fabric of finality which the human heart desires, yet they are not without significance for him who seeks the meaning of things.

While the fundamental mystery of life remains as mysterious as ever, the manifestations of living are each year becoming better known. Each year the light of scientific inquisitiveness illumines more brightly not only the creatures of today but also those of many a lengthy yesterday. For life left a trail in the mud of the past which grew more distinct as the eons slipped away. To retrace its devious winding is to relive the most exciting drama ever enacted in the theatre of time. It is also to wonder what the drama means.

The student of earth history sees in retrospect what could never have been foretold. Life was a new experiment under the sun, a new experiment possibly under any sun. A bit of jelly quivering to the surge of the sea might scarcely have been suspected of power to alter the earth. It achieved all but the impossible when it ate and spawned and grew strong in a violent world, when it faced the tumult of the waves and survived, when it faced the tumult of every environment for ages unnumbered and did not die.

If there is any meaning for mice or men in the restless drive of life, a billion years of living should contain it. To search those years for that meaning will be the object of this book.

Chapter I

IN THE BEGINNING

H<small>E</small> who stands on the island of knowledge, angling in the dark waters of the unknown, may watch the answers to unsolved problems moving by. Among the shoals he may soon descry a form which is larger and lustier than the others, which many before him have seen and sought to lure into the light. But the form will elude his every art and ingenuity as it has eluded them so many times before. For it is the answer to the problem of the origin of life, wiliest of all the swimmers in the sea.

Some men have been content to let the swimmer go his way. They have seen in him a sacred symbol of power greater than man; of power which man may never understand, which possibly man was never meant to understand. Other less reverent and more curious ones have gone stubbornly on with their angling, trying to win a flash of scales and hoping against hope for ultimate capture.

The making of myths has ever been a phase of angling. Variously the ancients sought the source of life in fire, water, air, and earth; and variously they found it there. They found life the haphazard offspring of chance, and the intended child of a god. They found, in short, poetic outlet for their varied fancies, but they left the answer to the problem in the sea.

Though the human mind has since been borne on the waves of light to many far recesses of the cosmos, the answer to the problem of the origin of life remains just out of reach. Myths still cluster around it. Most alluring of these is that life itself is a cosmic phenomenon, every-

6

where adrift in the waste of space; as primal as energy and with no more of a beginning, as enduring as matter and with no earlier prospect of an end.

By thus begging the question of origin, the cosmozoic myth need only explain the wandering of life in space and time. Thousands of meteors fall each day into the atmosphere of the earth, scattered shards of worlds beyond our own. Richter and Kelvin saw these as vehicles capable of conveying the germs of life throughout the universe. One-celled plants and animals today are able to grow protective shields against unfriendly environment, within which with abated vitality they may endure the rigors of heat, cold, and desiccation. Whether such living things might indefinitely so exist in the cold of space is a question without a scientific answer. More than one scientist has more than half believed they might.

Less easy to believe, however, is that a meteor freighted with the seed of life might safely land its cargo on such an air-swathed planet as Earth. For meteors burn in the atmosphere of Earth, and the few that run the gauntlet to the crust are deeply scarred. Arrhenius found this fact too great a burden even for a myth. But loving the myth he summoned his ingenuity to strengthen it, and succeeded. Not meteors, he said, but the radiant energy of light from the nearest star propels the uncoached germs of life through interstellar space. Potentially immortal in the absence of moisture and heat, they ride the sunbeams until they near a proper planetary home. Slowly then they sink through the air with the gentle pull of gravitation on their tiny bodies, escaping the hazard of death in the friction of a meteoric rush.

The remarkable persistence of this pretty fancy in the face of advancing knowledge is partly because it is poetic and appealing, partly because it cannot be conclusively disproved, but largely because all attempts to explain life in other ways have failed. Yet the assumption that life has always existed, or that it originated in some corner of time and space completely beyond the reach of curiosity, is hardly an explanation. It is only a romantic way of shutting the mind to the problem.

The assumption, on the other hand, that life was born of the only world it is surely known to inhabit runs foul of a dilemma. Ever since Pasteur so conclusively showed that a sterile medium does not give rise to living organisms today, most biologists have clung to the conclusion that spontaneous generation is impossible. But proof of a universal negative is also impossible. If life did not always exist, if it was not originally wafted to Earth ready made, it must have arisen there by spontaneous generation. "All life from the living" must have had at least this initial exception.

Those who have believed the living jelly different only in complexity from the inorganic earth have attempted to establish another exception. They have attempted to create life in a test tube. From the ancient alchemists with their aborted homunculi to the modern chemists with their not quite living colloids, each of these ambitious ones has failed. The best the godlings of the laboratory have achieved is the artificial fertilization of eggs; osmotic mineral growths with many of the properties of living things; the manufacture from inorganic materials of such normally organic substances as urea, indigo, thyroxin, and Vitamin D.

Undismayed by such relatively meager accomplishments, certain biochemists continue to challenge the law of biogenesis. Because little more than a century has passed since Wöhler first synthesized an organic compound, they have faith in the ultimate synthesis of protoplasm itself. Others, however, are less hopeful. They tend to believe that time in some subtle fashion did what they cannot do, or that conditions impossible to reproduce today existed when life first came to Earth.

II

Some scientists are convinced that the only barrier to the spontaneous generation of life today is the life that already exists. Refusing to be awed by Pasteur's stringent dictum, they think that life may even now be rising from the inorganic muck, but so slowly or so subtly that human eyes cannot detect it. In the complex chains of carbon atoms that fleck the lifeless world, in the strange bacteriophages that lurk beyond the vision of the microscope, they sense the undying creativeness of Nature. These things may be organisms in the making—half-living molecules that swarm to the boundary of the living world where they are stopped by the hungry creatures on the other side. Kill all plants and animals now alive, they say, and new life will rise to replace them.

In keeping with this conviction is the belief that the earth was essentially the same when life first came to it as it is today. Indeed, the conditions which have furthered life through time also might reasonably have brought it into existence. Accordingly, Allen has painted a picture of lightning aflame in the damp primordial air, producing ammonia and the oxides of nitrogen as it does today. Washed to the ground by rain and thence by rivers to bodies of standing water, these air-born chemicals mingled with earth-born sulphates, chlorides, phosphates, and carbon dioxide. Thus were assembled all the ingredients of living creatures but life.

Into the pudding the sun stirred ferment. The nitrogen sucked oxygen from its compounds and gave it to the air;

the elements recombined. What the sun began, the unstable compounds of nitrogen continued. Ferment never ceased until there came eventually the combination known as protoplasm with the properties known as life. Trading first in energy derived from the compounds of nitrogen, the nascent slime soon came to rely on the unfailing energy of the sun. It began to hoard energy in a manner prophetic of plants. Finally it became organized in cells, and life was truly launched. Even so today, says Allen, would life be freshly starting, if only the creatures already born were not so jealous of their birthright.

Here, however, the skeptic shakes his head. Anyone who knows how life was made should be able to make it. Let Troland stir a fortuitous enzyme into the pudding to speed the action toward its goal; let Osborn free the electrical energy of the elements; let any man alter the recipe to suit himself, but let him do it in the laboratory. Let him demonstrate the creation as well as describe it.

Though no recipe that man has ever made has ever worked, the one that Nature once concocted did. So the cosmic cooks defy the skeptic's taunt. They continue to theorize about the missing formula though they abandon the attempt to discover and apply it. Unlike Allen, most of them believe life the product of an earth quite different from the present one. With different ingredients in a different kitchen, it was probably first prepared.

Allen is typical of those who believe life the offspring of a cool earth built up in accordance with the planetesimal hypothesis. Pflüger, on the other hand, represents those who believe it the child of dying fires on the old Laplacian globe. Were cosmogonists less vacillant in their views Pflüger's theory would now be out of date. But cosmogonists discarded the nebular for the planetesimal hypothesis, only more recently to move with Jeans and Jeffries toward a fusion of the two. Belief in a formerly incandescent globe is consequently once more in style.

Studying the vast difference between dead and living protein, Pflüger concluded that it was due to the strange combination of carbon and nitrogen which chemists call cyanogen. This radical is invariably involved in the changes · that living protein undergoes. Because in its formation a large amount of heat is absorbed, cyanogen possesses a large amount of energy. It is this energy that animates the flesh.

Since cyanogen arises only in incandescent heat, life must have been born of fire. Compounds of cyanogen combined with compounds of carbon, and these with the other salts of protoplasm when later the earth was sufficiently cooled. Thus with its basic properties established, life was ready to expand down the ages in myriad forms and functions.

And so, like life itself, the theories to explain it have expanded to the present. Modern astronomers rather generally believe in the cosmic evolution of matter. From the "unclothed atoms" of Eddington, which lie stripped of their electrons in the hot inner privacy of stars, matter is thought to range with falling temperature through the atomic form to the form of simple compounds. When sufficiently cool it shapes to those complex and relatively rare compounds that grow only in the presence of water. Eventually it arrives at what may be the rarest—as it certainly is the most complex—condition of all: matter in the form of living flesh. In such a continuous chain, life is a link with a definite position.

Accordingly, the consensus of modern scientists inclines toward a definite and single birthday for life at a time when the earth was quite different from the earth today. It imagines a globe with a thinner atmosphere soaking in the radiation of a hotter sun. It sees it suffering a vast bombardment of alpha particles shot from the guns of radioactive substances, and of ultra-violet light hurled down from the sky.

The power of ultra-violet light is just now coming to be understood. That it can actually produce sugar and other organic compounds from the muck, without the aid of leaf green, is a recently established fact. These rays, today so largely checked by the oxygen in the air, may have beaten with vigor on the primordial globe, stirring up many reactions which later ceased to take place.

They may have thickened the seas with carbohydrates and formamides to the consistency of soup. In this soup there may eventually have come the first bit of protoplasm that could eat and reproduce. As to how it was activated to the living state and what were the steps in its early evolution, contemporary theories are neither clear nor agreed.

But the voice of the skeptic is as unequivocal as ever. All this, it says, is only the old enigma in the dress of a newer day. It no more explains the origin of life than analysis of paper and ink explains a poem.

III

Sooner or later in searching the earth for her history, the geologist arrives in Ontario at the shores of Rainy Lake. Beneath his feet are the oldest rocks that convulsion or erosion have anywhere exposed, rocks laid down as sediment in water nearly two billion years ago. So well have these so-called Coutchiching formations endured the varied travail of the ages that sun cracks and wave ripples, even the dimples of raindrops, have survived. Yet nowhere do they show the effects of excessive radiation. Rather do they tell of an atmosphere whose gases gnawed at the lands, whose showers made rivers that swept the riven fragments to the sea. They tell, in short, of an earth essentially like the earth today.

If life began when the air was thin and easily pierced by ultra-violet light, it must date from a day in the unknowable past before these oldest accessible rocks were formed. By the time of their deposition, life should already have had a history. Yet such fossils as record the existence of organisms through many a later epoch have not been found in the Coutchiching formations. Nowhere has the search of a century discovered a single signature of animal or plant. Strata preserving rainprints on a shore that was obviously friendly to life are as empty of life's tokens as the moon. Could it be that a new enigma has joined the old enigma of the origin of life—the enigma of life that somehow lagged in a world long ready to receive it?

Indeed, the suspicion of such a lag grows with the growth of knowledge. The Coutchiching is the oldest and simplest of many ancient and complex groups of rocks. Known collectively as the Pre-Cambrian, these formations are exposed in lavish confusion over more than one-fifth of the land area of the globe. A full two-million square miles of North America is theirs. Behind their ample but tightened lips are three-fourths of the secrets of terrestrial history.

Ever since Sir William Logan organized the Geological Survey of Canada in 1842, men have attempted to make the Pre-Cambrian speak. They have wheedled a grudging admission of treasure beyond the dream of avarice; of eons beyond the power of the mind to conceive; of mighty fret and turmoil in the adolescent world. But on one matter they have all but failed to shake the stony silence. The Pre-Cambrian formations are persistently reluctant to mention life.

They constitute a record which is rather generally garbled by the matter recorded: the hectic growth of the globe from childhood to maturity. Offspring of a restless star, the earth spent much of its inheritance while still comparatively young. Harrowed so fiercely and often by the wrath of Vulcan, strained and broken by the tempests in a shrinking globe, the Pre-Cambrian rocks might well have forgotten so slight and delicate a consideration as life.

Yet they do remember certain interludes of peace, when quiet waves were lapping quiet shores; when living creatures might easily have found broad tranquil fields for roaming, and for resting when their roaming ceased. As the Pre-Cambrian eras lengthened toward a close, these placid moods prophetic of the future gained in number and duration. They are best recalled by the Huronian rocks of Ontario and the Keweenawan system of Michigan; by strata of comparable simplicity and age in Texas, Newfoundland, and China; and especially by the unmutilated Beltian formations of Montana. From these geologists have hopefully sought, and hopefully continue to seek, the earliest records of life on earth.

Because they have assumed that life evolved from simple to increasingly complex forms, with plants in the vanguard of the march through time, they have expected to find in these ancient rocks at least the remains of simple plants. In Bavaria, Saxony, Bohemia, Hungary, Finland, and Canada, the search at first appeared to be successful. It unearthed certain odd hemispherical masses composed of alternating layers of serpentine and marble, which somewhat resembled the skeletons of primitive living organisms. In Logan's report of 1863, these objects were referred to as the polyps of fossil corals. Three years later, Sir William Dawson concluded that they were the fossils of gigantic one-celled animals. He dubbed them *Eozoön canadense*, and convinced a great many scholars that the "dawn animal of Canada" was the oldest record of life on earth.

Long thereafter textbooks exhibited enlarged cross-section drawings of *Eozoön*, each detail appropriately labeled with an anatomical term. But certain men refused to believe that these structures had ever been alive. They saw in the minerals of which *Eozoön* was made, and in the formations where it most typically occurred, evidence of profound alteration by heat and pressure. They held that *Eozoön* was not a fossil but a fraud. Polemics flared in the halls of the learned, which lasted, alas, for several decades. The skeptics slowly carried the fight until *Eozoön* was finally banished to the limbo of discredited beliefs.

It was banished, but not for long. Though *Eozoön* may never have lived as an organism, it apparently will never die as a problem. Quite recently it has risen from retirement to knock at the gates of scientific respectability, this time in the guise of a plant. Though Osann has carefully demonstrated its inorganic origin, though such sober authorities as Raymond of Harvard have persistently cried its shame, there are those who would let it enter. They would accept it as the prototype plant which scientists have ever hoped to discover, forgetting that hope spins a film on the eye.

The resurrection of *Eozoön* as a plant was furthered by the discovery of somewhat similar objects in younger Pre-Cambrian formations, which seem to have more valid claim to such an identification. Modern blue-green algae are primitive one-celled plants, closely resembling bacteria. Multiplying in chains and sheets of cells, they extract calcium carbonate from the water in which they live. Clinging to the layers of this material as they form, the tiny plants in time produce the concentrically laminated masses of stone called "water biscuits." On first seeing examples of living "water biscuits," Walcott of the Smithsonian Institution remembered similar structures in the Pre-Cambrian rocks of Montana. He promptly returned to gather many specimens, which he later described with great elaboration as fossil blue-green algae.

Others followed Walcott's lead. Calcareous algae have now been reported from Pre-Cambrian localities throughout the world. Unfortunately, it is impossible to identify the plants alleged to have produced these ancient objects. Any one of them might possibly have resulted from the inorganic processes that are known to have built somewhat similar concretions in later rocks. The current tendency is to accept them as genuine fossil plants, but to do so is to make what Huxley has called "an act of philosophic faith."

Alleged Pre-Cambrian animal remains have survived the scrutiny of critics no better than have the plants. Repeatedly rising to attention on waves of their discoverers' ardor, most of them soon enough sink back to the slough of false alarms. A few, however, linger in memory and text, cherished rather for their renown than for their authenticity.

Such are the objects from the Pre-Cambrian rocks of Brittany, which Cayeux described in 1894 as fossil radiolarians. They are microscopic globules of amorphous silica embedded in a matrix of quartz, so small that the published drawings of them are magnifications of from one thousand to twenty-three hundred diameters. One wonders how much error of interpretation may have entered so wide a breach. One wonders how such tiny and delicate skeletons could have escaped the admitted recrystallization of the rocks that contain them. One wonders why other investigators have rather generally failed to encounter similar remains in formations of comparable antiquity. And wondering so, one wonders why an occasional textbook should not wonder too.

Fossil sponges were described as early as 1911 from Pre-Cambrian formations in Ontario: hollow gourd-like masses of rock whose concentric layers are riddled by radiating tubes. Though some of these are probably mere counterfeits of the mineral world, products of the alteration of limestone by silica-laden water, others may possibly be bonafide fossils. Authentic, too, may be the casts of certain tube-like cavities, so widely believed to record the tunneling of worms along primeval shores. At least no one can definitely prove them spurious.

Organisms higher in the scale of life than sponges and worms have been reported repeatedly from Pre-Cambrian formations. Most have failed to survive a searching examination. Limestones of the Belt series in Montana are rich in dark markings suggestive of the chitinous skeletons of crustaceans. Unfortunately, almost none of these markings shows the regular outline and definite surface ornamentation which would place such identification beyond reproach. Raymond believes them truly organic, possibly the remains of seaweeds.

A few calcareous algae, seaweeds, sponges, and worms, any one of which may not be what it seems, is a meager testimonial of so imponderable a time. Once held to have been finished in a brief six days, the creation would appear to have been hardly begun at the end of a billion years. Three-quarters of the history of Earth to the present had been written before life came conspicuously into the record. Life does not lag behind its opportunities today. Why then did it lag in the beginning?

IV

In the early decades of geologic investigation, the widespread distortion of the Pre-Cambrian rocks would have seemed sufficient to explain their deficiency in fossils. But today we know that the prevailing turmoil of the time does not explain the paucity of fossils in strata that escaped it. Neither do any physical peculiarities in these strata, nor in the conditions under which they were formed, account for the strange ellipsis.

Walcott, whose eyes were among the keenest in the history of paleontology, spent nearly two decades in an all but fruitless search for Pre-Cambrian fossils. He finally concluded that most of the unaltered Pre-Cambrian strata had been born of lakes and rivers at a time when life dwelt only in the sea. Today this surmise seems as unhappy as the search that mothered it. Recent investigations have fortified belief in the marine origin of many of the mooted formations.

Because vast amounts of carbon in the form of graphite are disseminated through Pre-Cambrian sedimentary formations the world around—carbon which can best be explained by the decay of living tissue—most theories infer the existence of living creatures at the time and place of their deposition. Lane has suggested that chlorine and other chemicals made the ancient seaways acidic; that creatures, in consequence, failed to secrete the limy skeletons capable of recording their existence. Opposed to this view, however, are the calcareous algae which many believe were living in these ancient seas, untroubled by any dearth of available calcium. Opposed to it, too, are the mountains of limestone which formed as calcareous ooze in defiance of the alleged acidity of the water.

Chamberlin, whose imagination has enriched so many departments of geologic science, believed that life came first to the soil; that not until long eons later did creatures enter the limy waters of the ocean where skeletons might be built. No one can prove or disprove this suggestion. But one may wonder if creatures could possibly have failed to discover over half the surface of Earth during more than half their sojourn upon it. Besides, most thinkers have favored the sea as the primeval homeland of life. Water is the first need of life today, and was doubtless its first need yesterday. Then, as now, the sea was the only source of water that never failed.

Thus one by one the theories collapse. It is now rather generally agreed that the deposits of the Pre-Cambrian seas are widely and in places faithfully preserved in the rocks; that they commemorate conditions not demonstrably different from conditions today; that life, though largely unrecorded, existed in the seas when these deposits were formed. Theorists may no longer assume the contrary. They may no longer explain the paucity of Pre-Cambrian fossils through peculiarities in the environment. Failure to record the first billion years of its history must somehow have resided in the protoplasm itself.

Accordingly, Daly has imagined a primordial society so simple as to be essentially devoid of scavengers. Excepting only the bacteria, no hungry ghouls awaited the hour which fate had ordained for every living creature. Organisms sinking in death to the bottom of the sea stayed there to rot. The water steamed with ammonia born of decay, and this combined with the calcium in solution to form a limy ooze on the floor. Thus might the seas have been kept clean of such dissolved calcium as creatures could build into skeletons, until society had evolved a scavenging system.

The possible existence of lime-secreting algae in these supposedly limeless oceans is not the only serious objection to Daly's ingenious theory. Nature today forbids a waste of food. It is almost unthinkable that the creatures of any day could have ceased their eating without being promptly eaten in turn. Furthermore, the worms and crustaceans that swarmed in the seas of the following Cambrian period were largely scavenging animals. They were clearly not made in a day. The specialization of some and the degeneracy of others imply an ancient lineage. Their ancestors were doubtless pursuing their unholy ways down the maritime pastures of Pre-Cambrian time.

Raymond, in his address as retiring president of the Paleontological Society in 1934, voiced other less obvious objections. Food that is eaten does not disappear. Whatever the cycle of its alteration, it must ultimately yield to putrefaction. Consequently, the fouling of the oceans by ammonia might be expected to be no greater under an absence of scavengers than it is today. Besides, if the Pre-Cambrian seas had ever become fully ammonified, life as well as its calcareous wrapping would have disappeared.

v

Fearless in the face of failing theories, Raymond goes on to spin a new one. He begins with the old belief of Brooks and other zoölogists that life's first victories were won at the surface of the open sea. Heavy skeletons would there have been a needless burden, a burden which Nature saw fit to withhold. Only with the passage of an inestimable eon did creatures discover the ocean floor, where many of them settled to a life of shelled and sedentary ease.

Raymond is the first to suggest a reason for so revolutionary a change in habitat and habit. All animals and many plants ingest with their water and food more calcium carbonate than they can profitably use. The problem of eliminating this surplus mineral material has always been most successfully solved by active living. The most energetic organisms, both living and extinct, possess light siliceous or chitinous skeletons, or no skeletons at all. The sluggards carry the heavy shells. Unarmored creatures are not fleet from running for their naked lives, but naked because they love to run. The snail is not slow because he is safe within his shell, but shelled because he is slow. Thus Raymond reverses an ancient belief.

Much that is known of life in the Cambrian seas, where first it was adequately recorded, suggests that inactivity was only just beginning at that time. Most animals were lightly clad crawlers, floaters, and swimmers; few were tied together in phlegmatic colonies, or rooted to the ocean floor. Their Pre-Cambrian forbears were doubtless free and naked nomads of the sea.

Meat-hungry carnivores did not bare their teeth until the Cambrian period was all but spent. During the long heyday of the preceding eras unnumbered innocents reveled in an unvexed world. Time came, however, when the happy pastures grew congested; when the rising cloud of competition cast shadows over Paradise. Eventually the weak and the lazy were forced toward the bottom in search of a safer home. Many found death in the foodless depths of the dark abyss, others a new way of life in the shoals. There in peace the latter learned to crawl about for food, or to sit and wait until it drifted into their mouths. Able no longer to cope with the involuntary accretion of calcium carbonate, the more indolent began to grow shells. Theirs, the first fulsome record of life on earth, is not the story of a victory against the waves, but of a fall from grace; a geologic version of original sin.

Part of the business of being human is to costume somber facts in pleasing fancies. Nature is not content to round out our little lives with sleep, but must fill us with dreams while we are yet awake. We like to dream of worlds at either end of living where things shape nearer to the heart's desire. Raymond's theory, accordingly, should warm the cockles of the sentimental heart. In suggesting a time when the organization of society as well as the anatomy of individual members was not as it is today, when murder and parasitism and degeneracy may not have defiled the terrestrial scene, it implies an Eden without a serpent.

But to picture the Pre-Cambrian world as such a place is to falsify all we surely know of living. The creatures of the dawn may not have had our problems, but they doubtless had their own. Nature may safely be trusted to have held each age a trifle short of perfection. It is unthinkable that there might ever have been a time when she adequately cared for the output of her womb. Struggle and death must always have been the penalty for living, however differently they may once have been imposed. Such is the universal handicap of flesh. One creature alone has ever been known to escape it, and that one only in his dreams.

Chapter II

THE OTHER SIDE OF PROGRESS

T HUS science, philosophy, and fancy jostle one another
in the misty realm of beginnings. Each in its own favored
fashion is seeking the meaning of things. But the meaning
of things is a mischievous sprite who shows his face for a
moment and then is gone. For no one yet surely knows
how life began. No one can say that life is not as old as
time itself—nor as young as each newborn instant. It may,
for all we know, be both.

Life could not always have dwelt on earth because earth
was not always a suitable home. It may first have appeared
before the house was altered to its present plan, but exactly when and how it entered is a matter for conjecture.
And why it so meagerly recorded itself during more than
half its sojourn to the present is largely a matter for conjecture too.

In these fogs of uncertainty, however, certain truths
take shape. Though the precise condition of Pre-Cambrian
life must probably remain forever in the dark, certain tendencies of Pre-Cambrian living may be inferred. Chief
among these was the tendency for creatures to divide into
forces whose tactics in the battle of existence became totally
unlike.

Living is largely a dual business of capturing and re-
leasing energy. The split in the forces of life sent plants to
the business of capture, animals to the business of release.
The seaweeds and sponges in Pre-Cambrian rocks, if genuine, are the earliest tokens of this basic rift. In some
common ancestor the dominant qualities of both may once

have been equally blended, but that ancestor was not one of Nature's darlings. Nature did not even mark its grave.

In turning from the past to the present, however, we observe certain small soft-bodied creatures that came into the modern world without a fossil record. They suggest a possible condition of the flesh before the dawn of recorded history. Being at once both plant and animal, they are really neither. They are rather a strange third category of living things, a band of microscopic creatures that are devoted to an obscure general practice of life in a world where specialization is the vogue.

Low even in the company of these lowly creatures is the microscopic *Euglena*, which must solve every problem of existence by means of a single cell. As motile as any animal, it whips itself through the water with a threadlike lash of protoplasm. Like an animal it seizes food with its slit of a mouth, engulfing and digesting it in the liquors of its body. But it is also green with chlorophyl, which is the blood of the vegetable kingdom. By the strange magic of this material it can feed like a plant on the crudest fundaments of the inorganic world when fancier food is scarce.

If *Euglena* is taken to epitomize one of the earliest stages in the history of life, the slime-molds may be thought to commemorate a somewhat later stage. Almost formless masses of living jelly, the slime-molds lie like sticky felt on decaying logs and leaves of the forest floor. Though a single individual may be a full foot square and inches thick, there is no division of the body into cells. Like some gargantuan amoeba the monster rolls and flows in slow but ceaseless movement, sometimes sending out a lobe to engulf a mass of putrid offal, sometimes merging like a blob of syrup with another of its kind. At other times it sounds to the depths of a rotten log, its body dispersed in numberless streams which eventually merge on the other side to move once more as a unit. Devoid of chlorophyl, the slime-mold eats and moves like an animal.

It achieves its only grace during periods of reproduction. Then its sporangia rise in a Lilliputian forest of delicate stalks, which are severally capped by knobs or cups or umbrellas full of spores. When ripe the dainty capsules break. Unmindful of the sodden future that awaits them, the spores dance forth on the wind. But only too soon do these Ariels grow into Calibans. They settle in slime where they hatch into creatures which are both, which can both dance like the whip-lashing *Euglena* and creep like the amoeba. Eventually they pair and give rise to microscopic replicas of the unlovely thing that mothered them. Thus, though the slime-mold eats and moves like an animal, it breeds like a spore-bearing plant.

The bacteria, too, defy the categorical distinctions that hold among organisms of higher caste. They are mere pin points of protoplasm, molded to the form of a ball, a rod, or a screw. In a single inch, ten thousand of these smallest of creatures might lie in comfort end to end. Physiologically, however, they rank among the most complex and highly specialized of all living things. Some of them writhe and feed like one-celled animals; most of them dwell as saprophytes and parasites in the manner of yeast and other lowly plants. Though usually classed in the vegetable kingdom, bacteria are devoid of chlorophyl. Some of them can live on such doubtful delicacies as hydrogen sulphide, petroleum, arsenic, ammonia, and iron, which no other creatures—whether plant or animal—will touch.

Thus freely does Nature allow a few of her children to jump the fence that divides her living kingdom. Sparingly she grants somewhat similar privileges to others. She permits such animals as sponges to sit through their days as stolid as any plant; to diatoms and the sensitive plants she has given respectively the freedom of movement and the delicate reactions of animals. She tinges a few of her sponges and worms, but not one of her fungi, with green. She strengthens her sea squirts with the cellulose of a plant and some of her algae with the stony support of an animal.

She does all this, however, with no wide departure from the plan she laid down at the start. That plan was to sunder the living into plants and animals, and to keep it sundered forever. The few exceptions to the plan are of little significance in the swarming tide of creation.

To sit in the sun and store the energy of air and earth, or to steal this energy and roam the world—these are the two basic ways of existence. To one or the other nearly all live things from the beginning have been made to conform. With infinite variety of detail their bodies were molded to but two fundamental designs. Those that were chosen for the one were blessed with the peace of simplicity; those that were chosen for the other were cursed with the plague of unrest. Dull and inactive, alert and free, the two have moved down the pathways of time—to the quiet beauty of a flower and the brilliant promise of a brain.

II

Belief in a universal urge toward change is deeply rooted in modern science. Half a century before physicists began to demonstrate the eternal fluxing of the physical world, biologists had demonstrated the instability of flesh. When Darwin shattered the old creationist doctrine of fixity in the realm of the living, he gave men a new lens for viewing the displays of Nature. Through it they could see the world, which many previously believed to have been cut and dried in a week, as still in the making after two billion years.

A spectacle that once seemed as frozen as a statue now appeared as fluid as a dance. Even scientists became as blind to the stable elements of the composition as before they had been blind to its changes. For, once discovered, the moving objects in any panorama charm the eye; the background acts chiefly as a frame for the dynamic elements of the picture. Today, in viewing the vista of life against the background of its limitations, the eyes of scientist and layman alike are still charmed by the marvelous predilection of living creatures to change. The equally remarkable tendency to resist change lies largely unobserved.

Paradoxical as it may seem, the reactionary proclivities of protoplasm are as much a factor in evolution as its instability and flux. When in the beginning Nature built a wall between the kingdoms of plants and animals, she also built lesser walls between the various clans within each kingdom. After untold eons these walls, for the most part, still stand.

The algae and ferns of today differ only in minor details from the algae and ferns of half a billion years ago; in every fundamental of anatomy and physiology, the earliest and the latest seed-bearing plants are one. Though widely different in detail, crustaceans now and in the beginning were cast in identical molds. Every fundamental distinction between modern echinoderms and molluscs was firmly established among the earliest prototypes of these two great groups. Evolution, in short, very early neglected the fundamental structure of life and devoted itself to modelling the details.

To explain these facts Dr. Austin H. Clark of the United States National Museum has advanced an ingenious hypothesis. The driving forces of life, whatever they may be, urged protoplasm at the very beginning of its existence from the status of the primitive cell into a host of different forms.

Relatively few of these forms were capable of survival. Those that were became the prototypes of the major groups of plants and animals; unsuccessful intermediate types perished at birth. Thus definitely outlined at the start of their racial history as the only possible vehicles of life, the major groups proceeded to move essentially unaltered down the ages.

Clark derives an explanation for the rigid delineation of the various groups from the early embryological development of living animals. Every living animal, regardless of its complexity when mature, begins life as a single cell. With growth the cell soon reaches a stage where it can no longer function as a unit. It divides into two cells, which in turn divide into four; and thenceforth on and on as long as growth is possible. The dividing cells may follow but three different channels of development. They may be severed with each division so that the individual animal is always composed of a single cell. Such animals are known as protozoans. Or, instead of separating with each division, the cells may adhere in the irregularly radial clumps of protoplasm that are known as sponges. Finally, the cells may proliferate in a series of geometrical designs which give rise to various groups of more complicated structure.

All the animals in this third and largest department pass through identical changes in the beginning of their individual life histories. Soon after the initial cleavage of the egg from which each one is derived, a coral, a starfish, a snail, a worm, a shrimp, and a man, are each but a hollow ball of cells. This ball which is known as a blastula then collapses, and becomes a cup called a gastrula. From the gastrula stage the members of the various groups diverge along their several paths which never again come together.

Because so many animals pass through the gastrula stage before they differentiate, Ernst Haeckel long ago concluded that the earliest stable form in the evolution of multicellular animals must have resembled a gastrula. The group which includes the corals and the jellyfishes, and which most closely approximates the primitive radial symmetry of the gastrula, is assumed to have come to rest very near this latest stage which is common to all. The various groups of worm-like creatures diverged farther from the condition of radial symmetry, and in doing so they also diverged from one another. Similarly, such groups as the molluscs, the echino-derms, the arthropods, and the vertebrates, which came nearest to achieving perfect bilateral symmetry, did so by following their own peculiar avenues of development. These avenues represented the comparatively few ways of living that were economically feasible, and each was distinct from its neighbors after the gastrula stage was left behind.

Thus, according to Clark, sponges did not grow out of protozoans by gradual elaboration, nor did the more com-plex groups spring from one another. All came independ-ently and simultaneously into being. The hypothesis does not deny evolution, but merely restricts it to the lesser divisions of each group, where alone since the beginning of geologic history it is surely known to have occurred. It does not deny such lines of progressive specialization as that which led by subtraction and modification of an-atomical details from the small four-toed *Eohippus* of the Eocene epoch to the large one-toed horse of today. It only suggests that, spectacular as such sequences may be, they are narrowly and rigidly limited.

Whether Clark's explanation of the facts is right or wrong, resistance to change is an indubitable tendency in living things. The major adjustments of every organic group from the one-celled plants to the backboned animals were motivated by nothing that can be identified as am-bition, nor were they noticeably amenable to change when once they were made. On the contrary, the absence of any tendency to alter the fundamental design in the fabric of life is one of the most obvious (though least observed) aspects of organic history. Belief in the universal fluxing of creatures fits poorly with these facts. Belief in the universal urge to self-perfection does not fit at all.

III

It would seem to men, who alone are privileged both to sit in the audience and to act upon the stage, that strutting and fretting are the very gist of the drama of existence. To move, to be sensitive, and to change, is for them the definition of living. Perhaps it is why they overlook the fact that not all the actors have been cast to strut and fret their hour upon the stage, then to be heard no more. Many neither strut and fret, nor do they make a hurried exit. While with changing scenes and protagonists the play wears interminably on, they merely stand in silence in the rear.

The freezing lethargy which so early in their geologic history took hold like a leech on the plants and on every major group of animals was not content to stop there. Within each group whole classes and orders, as well as innumerable families, genera, and species, have known the tyranny of torpor. So many, indeed, have been those that in one way or another fell prey to it, that its influence must be counted a significant phase of the adventure of living.

It is not surprising that in the mêlée of time's unrest so many creatures should be altered by the hardships they endure. Sailing a sea where change alone is changeless, they must tack with the wind. The surprising thing is that so many should hold to so straight a course, and so long withstand the fury of the storms. Some fifteen percent or more of all the genera of invertebrate animals have somehow withstood for two or more geologic periods not only every threat of extinction but also every urge to change.

It is not enough to say that isolation far from the active strife of the world might explain these sluggard groups, for many of them have lived at the very centers of conflict. Better to say that something inherent in their flesh had kept them safely primitive, deaf to the dangerous challenge of change; that by failing to make any rigid adjustment to any one demand of a fickle world, they were able to meet each different demand as it was issued. What it was, however, that kept them so, no one may yet claim to understand.

When, for example, in the Tertiary period, the mammalian hordes were rising to the conquest of the land, the nautilus was born to a race that was losing its dominance in the sea. Today the success of the former is no more striking than the failure of the latter. Nautilus alone of the once mighty nautiloids lingers on, unshaken by the sentence of death which had been imposed upon his kind.

When earlier the dinosaurs were swarming in the swamps of Cretaceous lands, the little shells of the one-celled *Globigerina* were myriad in the seas. Today the dinosaurs are remembered only by their bones, but the *Globigerina* still batten in the sea—unaltered and undiminished by the tribulations of a hundred million years.

Long before any animal had ventured toward the land, in the dim dawn of Ordovician time, the shellfish *Lingula* buried himself in the mud. Like Santayana's Puritan he found it reassuring to be unobserved, even when doing nothing morally wrong. Unchanged today after five hundred million years, he is still in the mud off the coast of Japan. While mountains were rising and falling and rising again, while oceans were invading and retreating from the lands, while climate was endlessly swinging between tropic warmth and glacial cold, *Lingula* sat in the mud with professorial calm. He is history's outstanding example of stagnation.

Even the vertebrates, most variable of animals, include certain types which have stood still while eons rolled over their heads. The lung fishes of modern Australian rivers are little different from the lung fishes of Devonian bayous where backboned creatures first struggled toward air and land. The Port Jackson shark has swum from the Jurassic period to the present without any fundamental alteration of physique. The lizard which New Zealanders call the tuatera is an only slightly modified descendant of reptiles that antedated the dinosaurs.

Living fossils such as these deny any universal urge in the flesh toward specialized excellence. They prove that specialized excellence is not only unnecessary but decidedly hostile to the achievement of racial longevity. Not unlike the germ cells of mice and men which remain primitive and vital while other cells grow toward complexity and death, the static races endure while the progressive perish. The lives of the simple and the sluggish have length if nothing else.

IV

So many are the devices of stagnation that even those creatures that escape a living death in an unevolving species may yet fall foul of a similar fate in other ways. Some animals sink to the bottom of the sea and like plants send roots toward the mud, content to live on any food the vagrant currents may wash into their mouths. Others lie too sodden even to anchor themselves against the storms. Many gather together in phlegmatic colonies, made solid by cement secreted in their bodies; many others vegetate alone in burrows. Not a few grow skeletons that are more a snare than a support. So many and so easy, indeed, are the descents to Avernus that a majority of creatures in every age have travelled their treacherous ways.

The very oldest good record of an animal society reveals a tendency that tightened its grip on the flesh with the passage of time. Crustaceans, jellyfishes, worms, and molluscs, abounded in the seas of the Cambrian period. Most of them were lightly clad and active. But with them were sponges, cystoids, and certain coral-like creatures that clung in indolence to the bottom; and many a shellfish that burrowed in the mud. Though numerically slight in the society of their day, these stagnant ones were the first of a horde that was destined to degrade society in the days to come.

Benefits which are benign in moderation tend to become malignant with over-indulgence. Even the casual observer may see that the tendency of protoplasm to encase itself in mineral matter is a property fraught with danger. A light skeleton might well be advantageous in the fight against a hostile world. A heavy skeleton, though not necessarily a handicap in the struggle to live, is a very emblem of death so far as progressive enrichment of living is concerned.

Whether torpor in the earliest forms of life paved the way for the earliest skeletons, or whether the possession of skeletons made torpor inevitable, are questions as yet without any certain answers. It is only sure that torpor and skeletons have always been closely related; that the creatures which have carried the heaviest skeletons were generally the most sedentary and unprogressive of their race and day. On the contrary, not a few of the creatures that most successfully met the exigencies of their environment were devoid or nearly devoid of shell and bone.

In any systematic survey of the animal world a beginning is invariably made with the one-celled organisms which are technically known as protozoans. These "first animals" were so labeled on the twin assumptions that they were first in their appearance on earth and first in the simplicity of their bodies. Both assumptions, however, are open to certain objections and qualifications. Neither direct nor inferential evidence strongly supports the first, for, as Dr. Clark has shown, all the chief subdivisions of the animal kingdom may have originated simultaneously. As for the second, the simplicity of the protozoans goes little beyond their anatomy. In most other regards they are as complex, varied, and highly specialized as any other group of living creatures.

Protozoans, in fact, might well be defended as "first" in the variety and success of their adaptations to the world they inhabit. And it is significant that they win nearly all their triumphs without benefit of skeleton. Relatively few of them possess any hard parts whatsoever. These few, to be sure, have been successful enough in meeting the whims of time and weather, but no more successful than countless of their brethren who traveled naked.

There is no greater contrast in the living world than the contrast between the one-celled protozoans and the sponges. All protozoans are free to wander, and most are entirely unhampered by mineral secretions; all sponges are anchored to the earth, and most are loaded with skeletal material. No other large dynasty of creatures has ever been more generally or more heavily endowed with hard parts than have the sponges; no other has been more phlegmatic and unprogressive. Sponges are living vases of innumerable designs into which water and food enter through canals in the walls, and leave through large openings at the top. They have sat for eons on the table of the earth, too heavy to move and too tired to evolve, the outstanding examples of the bane of torpor and the outstanding indictment of skeletons as a hindrance to richer living. Though by enduring so long they may be said to have succeeded, theirs has been the pale success of a vegetative thing. Naturalists, indeed, failed to recognize the sponges as animals until the middle of the nineteenth century.

Corals and coral-like organisms are much like the sponges in appearance, but they are more advanced anatomically in the possession of muscle tissue and stinging cells with which they paralyze their prey. Their roots go deep in time. Ever since the middle of the Ordovician period the corals have been lavishly endowed with skeletons. No one can say that they have not thriven, but they have done so on a relatively low level within their group. A much higher level of success has been achieved by their relatives, the jellyfishes, who have retained their heritage of free locomotion unhampered by excess baggage.

The creatures that pass in ordinary parlance as worms are extremely varied both in appearance and in the lives they lead. Excepting the few that possess horny jaws and body bristles, or that live in tubes of lime carbonate or agglutinated sand, the worms have lived without skeletons and have managed very well. They will doubtless long continue to assist in the demise of more cumbersome associates.

Among the populous society of spiny-skinned marine invertebrates, the extinct cystoids and blastoids and the now nearly extinct crinoids were all encased in stone and rooted like plants to the bed of the sea. The still living starfishes, brittle stars, and sea urchins were never so heavily armored, and consequently have always been freer and more effective organisms. The sea cucumbers, practically devoid of skeletons, are easily the freest and most effective of all.

The moss animals and the lamp shells have slight importance in the world today. The filigreed colonies of the
former are not uncommon along the seashore, attached
to rocks and weeds; the shells of the latter, which resemble
Roman lamps, exist in considerable variety in modern
oceans. But neither is apt to be often seen, except by the
eye of the specialist. Any midwest schoolboy with a ham-
mer and a collector's instinct, on the other hand, may hack
from the rocks the fossil remains of as many of these creatures as he desires, for they were legion in bygone days.
Throughout the long Paleozoic era they spawned so riot-
ously in the friendly seas that their numbers probably
equalled and possibly exceeded those of all their contemporaries combined. Yet during their lengthy sojourn on
earth not one species succeeded in rising far above the sluggish level of a vegetable existence. Crusted in shell and
anchored to the nearest object, they slept through time.

So too have slept a majority of the molluscs. Clams and
snails have cluttered the earth for ages, just sitting or wearily
crawling under the weight of their shells. The squids and
squidlike creatures are kinsmen of a different stripe, for
they escaped both lethargy and the burden of a heavy
skeleton. Sensitive and swift, they are the finest of their
clan.

Swift and sensitive, too, are many crustaceans, spiders,
and insects that walk on jointed legs and constitute the
greatest subkingdom of animals in the world. When so
many of their cousins were bogging down in the sea, these
creatures were rising to the mastery of every environment.
With skeletons of chitin which are generally flexible, light,
and strong, they have become not only the most numerous
multicellular animals on earth today, but also—in the person
of the insects—possibly the most successful as well.

Backboned animals have been generally more successful than the invertebrates in achieving the dual desiderata of mobility and sensitivity. Their skeleton is characteristically a dynamic mechanism inside their body, rather than a crust on the outside. Yet even these have known the bane of stagnation and the excessive secretion of mineral material. The bony-headed ostracoderms of Devonian seas and the heavy-footed amblypods of Eocene uplands, to mention but two examples, were biologic mistakes. They foundered into extinction under the weight of their own bones.

In view of these facts skeletons may hardly be considered unmitigated blessings, nor the organisms that first acquired them the heralds of a great achievement. The point beyond which a skeleton passes from a protection to a curse is not always easy to determine; that the point has been surely and frequently passed, however, no one familiar with the story of the rocks may deny. In one way or another the tendency to excessive secretion of mineral material has threatened most creatures since the dawn of organic history. It even threatens man. For when a man's arteries grow heavy and brittle with the carbonate of lime, he is experiencing a special phase of what has ever been one of the gravest and most universal hazards of living.

V

About a century ago, the eminent embryologist Ernst Von Baer made a mistake which might easily have condemned a lesser man of science. He bottled some embryos of backboned animals and neglected to label the bottles. When later he examined his specimens, he was unable to decide whether they had been taken from reptiles, birds, or mammals. Pondering his predicament, he was struck by the fact that animals as dissimilar as black and white in their adult forms might be as similar as peas in a pod during the early stages of development. Thus by accident, as has so frequently happened, he blundered upon a significant truth.

He further observed that the foetal forms of such land animals as men, rabbits, lizards, and hens, not only resembled one another but also strongly suggested a fish. In each one of them the heart, blood vessels, nerves, and the slits in the sides of the neck, were unmistakably fish-like. Half a century later, when the concept of evolution had broken like sunrise on the world of science, these facts fell into a pattern with a meaning. Air-breathing vertebrates were descended from gill-breathing fishes, and in its embryonic history each one retold the history of its race.

The assumption was extended to include all varieties of animals, as well as many plants. Haeckel erected a "history of Creation" upon it, and called the theory the "fundamental biogenetic law." Where Nature had failed to record the genealogies of animals in the rocks, biologists supplied the missing information from a study of embryo or larva. Hyatt, Beecher, and many other paleontologists arranged the jumble of fossil molluscs in evolutionary sequences that followed the stages in the shell development of living descendants. Nowhere was the beauty of the new faith besmudged by doubt or dissension. Embryos and larvae were historians that could not lie.

Eventually, however, suspicion crept into the flock. While most naturalists were ardently passing along the paths of embryology ever deeper into speculation on the origin and relationship of animals, a few sat down to think. Two doubts disturbed their minds. First, an embryo that matures in a few weeks or months could hardly be expected to retrace every step in a racial history that may have been millions of years in the making. Many steps must needs be slighted or eliminated, with commensurate falsification of the evolutionary record. Second, each growing embryo may live only by adjusting itself to the conditions environment imposes upon it. In making such adjustments, it may pass through stages that no ancestor ever shared. And so, by excluding the true and admitting the spurious, the embryo is scarcely a reliable historian.

These and other misgivings made riot in the fold until it became all but disreputable to infer anything whatsoever from the study of embryology. The pendulum of opinion swung from intemperate faith to intemperate scepticism without stopping at an intermediate position where soundness is apt to reside. Happily today it rests more nearly at the vertical. While aware of the possibilities of error, scientists are rather generally convinced of the historical import of certain embryological facts.

Many of these facts point to a progressive loss rather than a gain of biologic excellence. This is a significant fact in itself, and one that has never been emphasized in proportion to its significance. The world is full of animals which as adults are sluggish or tied to the earth, but which in infancy are both active and unattached. The clam that buries itself in the mud once whirled like a top in the water. Many sponges, corals, and crinoids, that sit with stagnant dignity in their shells, in youth swam naked in the sea. It cannot well be argued that roving larvae are essential to the continuation of sedentary and rooted species. Many such species, especially among the corals, can reproduce asexually by the vegetable device of budding. It is more likely that the vigor of the larvae commemorates an ancient vigor of the race, a vanished heyday when both old and young were free.

VI

The concepts of progress, stagnation, and degeneracy are products of the human brain. They may be as meaningless to the gods that arranged the world as they are to the oysters that inhabit it. Anyone, accordingly, who uses such concepts in an attempt to understand the spectacle of Nature is in a sense committed to the error of anthropomorphism. Fear of making this error has held more than one naturalist to the tabulation of trivial and uncorrelated phenomena, and has loaded our libraries with a vast tonnage of insignificant observation. It has debased more than one scientist to the status of a photographic plate, and his thinking to the level of bookkeeping. It has driven scholars from the sentimental delusion that birds and flowers palpitate with human emotions into the egotistical delusion that man is wholly different and divorced from the rest of creation. In short, it has treated one category of ills by substituting another.

It has obscured the simple fact that the obvious differences between man and the other animals do not gainsay their obvious similarities. It is no denial of the uniqueness of man's mind to affirm that his physical needs are not very different from those of his lesser kin. Nor is it a repudiation of man's special adjustments to the world to admit that all other creatures have made their several adjustments to essentially the same world. When the bugbear of anthropomorphism rises to deny these truths, it should be clubbed into silence.

Of course, in calling the evolving and sensitive animals progressive, and the static and phlegmatic ones decadent, man shows by the words he chooses a preference for the category to which he himself belongs. Were oysters able to judge the situation, they might consider the stagnant ones well adjusted successes and the active ones merely the victims of St. Vitus' dance. But it really matters little what terms are employed to point the differences, so long as the differences truly exist. Since man alone is able to detect and describe them, he must do so after his own fashion. If his diction has a flavor of morality and egotism, at least the gods and the oysters are not apt to care.

In gauging a situation with reference to normality one must remember, if true perspective is to be maintained, that normality is a highly variable standard. A man infected with streptococci is in a condition that may be abnormal for him but quite normal for the streptococci. Similarly, an oyster rooted to the sea floor may be normal enough with reference to other oysters, but abnormal with reference to the dynamic squid or his own presumably active forbears. With reference to the unimpaired locomotive freedom which seems to have blessed the flesh in the youth of the world, a host of animals are abnormal. They are truly degenerate because of the qualities they have lost, regardless of how well adjusted they may now be.

By different pathways we thus converge to the belief that organic history is in no slight degree a record of stagnation and decay. Such progressive evolution as has led from the primitive primates to modern man has been relatively rare. The tendency to degenerate, on the other hand, appears from available records to be well-nigh universal. Not even the specialized progressive species have been free from its menace in one or another form; only one creature, so far as anyone can tell, has ever even been aware of it. And that creature has made small use of his awareness.

Like every other organism that ever lived, this one has become what he now is with little conscious direction of his own. Unlike all others, however, he possesses the capacity

for such direction. Latterly he has begun to suspect that
it might be well to use it. He has begun to suspect that
indifference to the welfare of his own species is hardly the
way to preserve that welfare in an indifferent world. When
he changed from a hunter into a farmer he did what the
clam had done before him. He sat down and exposed himself to the hazards of sitting down. He is now beginning
to realize that not only his body but his beloved soul and
institutions can sink like the skeletons of his lesser neighbors in the mire of stagnation and decay.

He is beginning to realize, in short, that things as they just
happen to be are not wholly to his liking. He is beginning
to attempt to break the laws that have chained all others
since the dawn of creation, and to set up new laws more
pleasing to his private tastes. He no longer shudders and
throws up his hands at what he sees in the world, nor
whispers in his own ear that it is not so. He only knows
with Thoreau that "Nature is hard to be overcome, but
she must be overcome."

He has raised his ax before the tragic framework of existence. Distressed and confused, he does not always strike
a telling blow. But at least he strikes, and therein lies his
hope.

Chapter III

THE MECHANICS OF SUCCESS

B<small>Y</small> implying motivation through purpose, success is a typical concept of the human mind. Men, who believe with some reason that their own behavior may be consciously purposive, have frequently inferred some comparable actuation for the behavior of other creatures. Inasmuch as no amount of undirected manipulation might conceivably create so intricate and useful a mechanism as a watch, it is difficult for men to believe that any amount of random activity might conceivably create so intricate and useful a device as a beehive.

It is easy for them, on the other hand, to assume that effort toward desired and envisioned ends is the power that drives the entire living world. Many, indeed, have so assumed, and a few like Henri Bergson have beautifully and persuasively urged the truth of their assumption. But the men who have seen most in the lives of plants and animals have rather generally failed to see there any convincing equivalent of human purpose. If they have seen any suggestion of divine purpose in a world of boundless cruelty and waste, they have rather generally yielded to others the embarrassing task of discovering its justification.

Biologic success is measured by the fitness of creatures for the lives they lead. With the sole known exception in man, the attainment of this fitness—so far as the science of biology may surely say—is as automatic as breathing during sleep. Neither the site nor the equipment of success may be consciously chosen or altered by species or individuals. Conditions just happen to combine in some cases to the advantage and in other cases to the disadvantage of the organism.

Since Darwin first anchored the doctrine of chance to a base of observable fact, innumerable observations and experiments have been made which in small part discredit but in large part confirm his views. Post-Darwinian investigations have added very little to Darwin's meager knowledge of the fundamental causes for the variations which underlie the fate of organisms. They have detracted little from Darwin's general argument for the shaping of that fate by environment and competition. Given the inventive fertility of flesh on an earth too lean to satisfy its needs and the stage would seem to be adequately set for the drama of life.

Most men do not enjoy finding economy where they have sought morality, especially when the economy seems uneconomical and cruel. That some chance advantage should have been at the bottom of every achievement in the living world for more than a billion years is a concept which they can scarcely stomach with pleasure. That the lucky should have ruthlessly and invariably pressed their advantages at the expense of the luckless is even less palatable to the moral taste. It is not surprising in view of the traditional inconsistency of that taste that many have preferred to exchange these bitter likelihoods for sweeter fictions.

Unfortunately, biologic success may not be reliably described with reference to the moral sense of man. Neither may it be reliably measured with reference to the human sense of time, space, and relativity. Practically speaking, there is no human sense of time, space, and relativity because only a few men think less briefly and parochially than they live. Were it possible to view the living world as Einstein has viewed the physical world, expanding the imagination to the size and complexity of the subject it attempts to grasp, the ramifications of biologic success and failure might appear both endlessly and indistinguishably interwoven.

For even the less cosmic eye may see that biologic success and failure are neither pure nor stable values. The clam who sits in the mud may be a failure with reference to the bird who flies in the sky, but he is also a success with reference to those who must die because he sits there. The tapeworm who has lost many organs through degeneration is in one sense a failure with reference to his ancestors who retained them. In another sense he has succeeded and his ancestors have failed because he is alive and they are not. Gauged by the relative duration of their existence, the sharks who ruled the seas for part of the Devonian period were less successful than the dinosaurs who ruled the lands for the whole of the Mesozoic era. But even the dinosaurs eventually perished. Gauged by the ultimate inevitability of death, all success is a phase of failure because all living is a phase of dying.

What, then, remains of success? Nothing essential, it would seem, but the ability to eat and to avoid being eaten until reproduction is attained. Any individual that reproduces before it dies, any species that propagates itself however briefly, completes the basic cycle of life and achieves thereby the one fundamental success. The stagnant and the degenerate, the spectacular and the dull, are all equally successful in the economy of Nature if they succeed in this. Paltry though such success may seem to those who are able to dream of higher goals, a great many individuals have failed to achieve it. The adaptations which have enabled some to succeed are the most marvelous phenomena in the world. They are also the most mysterious.

II

Everywhere one goes one may observe the perfection with which creatures are fitted for the lives they lead. Only rarely, however, is one permitted to observe the manner whereby this fitness comes into being. The statement that it has never been observed, indeed, has long been a popular cliché. Yet the statement is only partly true, as the case of the Yorkshire moths will show.

According to J. B. S. Haldane and other British naturalists, a large wood of pine and birch trees in Yorkshire was divided in 1800 by a strip of heather. Five years later the pines were removed from one division and the birches from the other. Animals inhabiting the wood accordingly found themselves in two different environments, one darkened by the subdued hue and thick foliage of the pines, the other brightened by the birches.

When the region was more recently studied by scientists, a species of moth consisting of both dark and light individuals was found to inhabit both environments. In the pine wood most of the moths were of the dark variety, in the birch wood most were light. Clearly the moths had become differentiated to harmonize with the colors of their respective homes.

There are three possible ways of explaining this differentiation. One is to assume that some mystical urge, either in the moths or in the deity that watches over them, impelled the parent moths to breed offspring that would be least conspicuous in their environment and hence least attractive to their enemies. This is the classic doctrine of vitalism which in one form or another has commanded adherents since Aristotle expressed his belief in it. Though there is sufficient sentiment to keep the assumption popular today, there is nothing that modern science may recognize as evidence to prove it.

Another explanation is that the environment directly molded the moths, that their involuntary responses to its influence led to gradual changes of color, that alterations thus acquired by one generation were transmitted to the next until the colors most appropriate for survival were attained. This is the Neo-Lamarckian interpretation. But in the Yorkshire case, as in so many others, the investigators failed to obtain any indication that environment might exert such an influence. Feeding the caterpillars of dark moth mothers on the wood of the birch did not tend to lighten the color of their offspring. Feeding the caterpillars of light moths on pine made the ensuing moths no darker than their parents.

There is, furthermore, a strong presumption derived from a multitude of experiments that the adaptive responses of individuals are not heritable. Though it has recently been established that X-rays may induce heritable mutations in insects, such mutations are random and generally disadvantageous. They are quite the reverse of the definite and advantageous responses to environment that are postulated in the Lamarckian hypothesis.

A blacksmith can will his shop to his son but not his strong right arm. The son of a mountaineer may inherit his father's shoes but not his bulging calves. If the environment might possibly have changed the color of the Yorkshire moths directly and advantageously in accordance with Lamarck's assumption, the moths could yet no more have bequeathed their new colors to their children than a woman could bequeath a coat of tan to hers.

The third explanation is that purely random forces, whether external or internal, arranged the hereditary characters in the germ plasm of the moths so that they were born of different colors; that those which did not happen to match their environment were foredoomed to die because they were congenitally unfit to live. By a masterful euphemism this harsh and wasteful process is known as "natural selection."

Though the environment may have induced heritable variations in the moths through bombardment of their germ cells by X-rays, it could not have induced colors appropriate for survival to the exclusion of colors that were not. Its chief work with reference to the observed adaptations of the moths was the selection of the appropriate and the elimination of the inappropriate colors *after* they had been produced. This is the Neo-Darwinian view.

The cogency of this explanation became apparent in the Yorkshire case when the uneaten wings of the dead moths were gathered and studied. For in the dark pine wood selective elimination was clearly at work. The living dark moths far outnumbered the living light moths, whereas among the dead the proportions were reversed. In the birch wood the opposite was true. In short, the birds and bats that prey on moths were feeding heavily on those of each generation that did not happen to match their background. It is not inconsistent with modern knowledge of the laws of heredity to suppose that eventually the strains of disharmonious color will be thus completely eliminated in the moths of both woods, so that all moths that live in the pines will be dark and all in the birches light.

The weakness of this explanation, as someone has phrased it, is that it accounts for the survival but not for the arrival of the fittest. It begs the fundamental question of how the different colors originated. To postulate their origin by chance is only to confess ignorance of their origin. But to postulate their origin through the desire of the moths or the dictation of the environment is to postulate what no one can prove.

Thus, just as the phenomenon of adaptation exhibits itself in the moths of Yorkshire, so too does the antagonism of the theories to explain it. Though the Darwinian factor is confessedly eliminative rather than creative, it is the only one that is widely substantiated by evidence of a scientific nature. The creative factors that operate in the living world may do so, at least in part, in accordance with Aristotelian or Lamarckian principles. Geneticists have told us much, but they have not yet told us how these creative factors are themselves created. Should they ever be able to do so, they will have solved the greatest enigma of life. Until they are able to do so, all theories of adaptation must remain unscientific, unfinished, and possibly untrue.

III

Before natural history grew up into biology the student of plants and animals went to the field to observe. Now for the most part he goes to the laboratory to experiment. The shift was more than a change of method and location. It was also a change of approach to the problems of Nature. One need not exaggerate the achievements of the naturalist or belittle those of the biologist to see that something valuable was lost in this evolution.

Gilbert White could not have known and probably would not have cared about the rôle of chromosomes in the genesis of earthworms. But he knew and cared about the rôle of earthworms in his little world of Selborne. He knew that life is more than the isolated facts and principles of anatomy, function, and descent. It is not always obvious that the specialist of today knows as much. He too often obscures the forest of life by magnifying the trees that compose it.

Stimulated by the evolutionary philosophy of Nature, modern biology stresses above all other relationships the anatomic and genetic relationships of living creatures.

From a professional point of view it is important to know that both spiders and flies have jointed appendages, but that the former has eight and the latter only six. Facts of this sort put spiders and flies in their proper anatomical and genealogical places with reference to one another, and also with reference to the rest of the living world.

Such facts, however, do not orient spiders and flies with reference to the dynamic business of living. They do not reveal the very different methods whereby the two make their bargains with a flinty world. The possession of jointed appendages does not constitute a bond of sympathy when the two meet, nor does the difference in the number of appendages determine the outcome of the meeting. However valuable such facts may be in disciplining the minds of freshmen and in labeling specimens in museums, they do not elucidate life as it is lived in the flesh. To know life only by such facts is like knowing football by the weight, position, and parentage of the players while remaining ignorant of the plays.

One is not apt to find the significant plays and rules of living in any of the conventional sciences of life. Life is far broader and less arbitrary than these sciences. Whole categories of data which they ignore are significant in a more realistic approach to living.

Especially significant in such an approach are certain basic patterns of existence which do not lie within the limits of any orthodox department of biologic thought and which cannot be explained by any orthodox theory of evolution. Theories of evolution, indeed, have practically neglected the similarities of creatures in attempting to explain their differences. The most striking aspect of these patterns is the universality with which they apply to the motley multitudes that people the earth. Again and again have creatures of dissimilar origin been similarly shaped to fit them. They embrace, in fact, all living things, the active and the progressive no less than the stagnant and the degenerate. They are deadly to the myth that Nature never repeats.

The trilobites that once ruled the earth, to be sure, are dead. They will almost certainly remain so to the end of time. The mole is not apt to regain its lost sight, the snake its legs, or the tapeworm its ambition. Nature has never been known to return a life, an organ, or an attitude, once she has taken it away. But in a general fashion she does repeat certain favorite designs for the bodies and behavior of her children.

She repeats because the world is not so variable nor are its inhabitants so various as they might seem from a specialized point of view. It is true that the compromises which creatures make with a shifting world and with one another are multiple and diverse beyond hope of complete enumeration and description. As long as men remain curious the catalogue of examples will doubtless grow. But it has already grown large enough to show that it does not grow at random. It expands by departments which are as rigid in form and limited in number as the items they contain are varied and abundant. It does so because these departments represent the only fundamentally different methods of living.

Whatever power may decide what kinds of individuals shall be born, environment decides to a considerable extent what kinds shall survive to maturity. Adjustment to the physical environment is life's first command. Unless this adjustment is successfully made, no felicity in the adjustment of a creature to his fellows can save him from destruction. Inasmuch as there are but few decidedly different types of physical environment, there are but few decidedly different designs for living.

Though in detail the earth has been changing these many eons and with it the creatures that have clung to its back, the sea and the land and the air have always existed somewhere since geologic history began. There have always been the sunlit surface waters of the sea where creatures might bask and drift at ease, the somber abyss where they might sink to a stagnant security, the turbulent shores where they might find their weakness and their strength.

On land there have always been the dynamic rivers to develop the dynamic powers of flesh, and the placid lakes to foster its placidity. There have been the swamps for amphibious pursuits, the plains and deserts for running, the hills for walking and burrowing. In the air there have always been buoyancy for those who could use it to fly, and more recently trees for climbing and leaping. Conspicuously in some cases and inconspicuously in others, these places and ways of living have placed their peculiar brands on all who have ever come under their jurisdiction.

IV

The sea, in the belief of many, was the earliest home of life. Certainly by the testimony of the geologic record it has long been the home of a numerous and varied society. The reason is not far to seek. The sea is the most dependable medium of life, the safest place to live. Its temperature and gases are relatively constant. Its water is much like the blood of its inhabitants, and it never fails.

Even the simplest performances of life are difficult on land. The mere act of going from here to there is made hard by the lightness of the atmosphere. Suitable food for most land animals is too heavy to float in the air. It stolidly clings to the ground. Animals must move to their meals through their own exertions, or steal a ride.

Living is more idyllic in the sea. Because water is 814 times as heavy as air and almost as heavy as protoplasm, sea creatures are all but exempt from the drag of gravitation. A bit of gas or a drop of oil and they become as airy as angels. One-celled plants and animals in untold billions float near the surface of the sea, like motes in a shaft of light. They live with ease themselves, and they enable their larger neighbors to do likewise.

Jellyfishes, molluscs, crustaceans, and certain diminutive backboned creatures have long abided in the sunlit paradise of the open ocean. Varied though they are in heritage, they have come through living alike to looking alike. They are uniformly unencumbered by heavy skeletons because buoyancy is the first requisite of their lives. They are characteristically shaped like parachutes rather than projectiles because they are moved by wind and current rather than by their own exertions. Their ineptitude as swimmers is offset by their ability to sink below the waves in time of storm and to rise when the storm subsides. Colorless as the water they inhabit, they represent a comparably colorless compromise between progress and stagnation.

Far both from the surface and the shore is the abyssal underworld of the sea. Live creatures have been caught in the dredges of the oceanographer at depths as great as twenty-six thousand feet. Representatives of every major group of organisms, excepting the green plants and the air-breathing animals, have been collected below the lowest limit of wave action and light. Of these the fishes are the most interesting because they show best the standardization imposed by the most unvarying environment in the world.

Like the other dwellers of the deep they appear not to have originated there but to have migrated from shallower zones at comparatively recent epochs of geologic time.

Though a few are quaintly fierce of face, most are frail and faded, flabby, slim, and small. A few are blind but many have saucerlike eyes for gathering such light as may come their way, and phosphorescence for enhancing it. Most of them possess elaborate feelers for additional guidance through the endless night of their lives. Descended variously from sharks, eels, herring, cod, and pike, they have been uniformly shaped by the uniformity of their strange environment.

The morphologists of the laboratory are inclined to consider such resemblances skin-deep and unimportant. They deplore the easy inaccuracies of slack observation which once made vegetables of sponges and corals merely because they are rooted to the ground, and which yet beget error in the establishment of genetic affiliations. But when the obviously dissimilar in blood are yet strikingly similar in body and behavior, the similarities may just possibly be as significant as the differences. It does not further the attempt to understand the mechanics of life to dismiss the similarities merely because it is fashionable to do so.

Some convergent resemblances, indeed, go very much deeper than the shallow externals of form and function. Only the amateur or the careless observer would mistake a swallow for a swift, but only a prejudiced or a blind one would deny a real resemblance in the "telescope eyes" of certain fishes and molluscs that live in the abyssal sea. Though fishes and molluscs belong to totally different divisions of the animal kingdom, the eyes project from the head like opera glasses in the deep sea forms of both. In both, the optical lens is large and far from the retina that receives the image, a marvelous adaptation for conserving the light of the depths.

The most remarkable aspect of this convergence is not that the same complex organs develop in widely different organisms, but that they also develop in different ways from different types of tissue. The eyes of the fishes originate in the brain and those of the molluscs in the skin. Those who seek evidence of a guiding intelligence in Nature should welcome these facts. A series of happy Darwinian accidents might conceivably have led once to an organ as intricate as a telescope eye. That a quite different series of accidents should do it again is all but too much for the power of belief, rugged though it is.

Whereas stagnation marks the creatures at the surface of the sea and degeneracy those at the bottom, no one condition would appear at first sight to characterize the hordes that live along the shore. They would seem to be as various as the moods of the region they haunt. Darting fishes and wriggling worms, barnacles clinging to the rocks and starfishes clambering over them, sea-anemones that are rooted in the sand, crabs that run upon it, clams that burrow beneath it—these are but a few of the diversities of the shore. At first sight it would seem that the only uniformity to be found in this cradle of evolution is the uniformity of divergence.

On second sight, however, it may be seen that the variable strand is invariable in one regard. Each day it is alternately bared to the air and buried beneath the water. The creatures that cling or crawl or dig in the tide-swept zone must alternately avoid being dried up by the air and driven away by the water. Animals dissimilar in blood have repeatedly achieved this ability. By doing so in similar ways with the help of similar organs they have come in not a few cases to resemble one another.

Seashores may be roughly classified as hard or soft. The inhabitants of rocky strands—seaweeds, limpets, barnacles, crabs, and a host of others—are universally hardened to withstand the pounding of the waves, and strengthened with organs of adhesion to resist the drag of the tides. Most creatures of sandy and muddy shores, on the other hand, either burrow or root themselves in the bottom. The clogging of their breathing mechanism is a daily threat. A great variety of molluscs, crustaceans, and other marine invertebrates have developed essentially the same sort of straining apparatus for protection against this menace.

The strongest animals that dwelt in the oceans during most of the periods of geologic history were those that were built for speed. Most of them came from the land where speed is a common commandment. The fishes were the first to go down to the sea from the rivers of the land, but they were followed in succession by a great variety of reptiles, birds, and mammals. The same type if not the same degree of change took place in all. Their bodies were streamlined toward the shape of a cigar. Their necks grew shorter, their tails longer, and their limbs became paddles or fins. Such surface adornments as ears, hair, feathers, and armor, tended to be smoothed away. Three different times in the history of life three different types of animals achieved perfection in marine locomotion: the shark, the ichthyosaur, and the porpoise. Though the first is a fish, the second a reptile, and the third a mammal, the three are so similar in form that a lay observer may fail to tell them apart.

v

The physical conditions of the lands above the shore are far more diversified and variable than those of the waters below it. Yet each of a number of conditions has repeatedly remained stable sufficiently long for the Procrustes of standardization to do its work. Even such comparatively evanescent environments as rivers, lakes, and swamps, have been known to stamp their inhabitants with their own peculiar marks.

All who would know the bounty of such places must meet one unvarying requirement. Salt is an indispensable ingredient of blood and it is apt to seep out of vessels which are in intimate contact with fresh water. The first need of all fresh-water animals is the ability to maintain the composition of their blood despite fluctuations in the composition of their environment. Unable to meet this requirement, such animals as sharks and their relatives are rare in rivers and lakes. Many other animals of diverse origin, however, can turn the trick. Their ability to do so creates a true blood relationship which is wholly independent of ancestry.

Lean in salt, fresh waters are likewise lean in buoyancy. Their people as a result are uniformly smaller than the people of the denser sea. Because the bodies of water are also for the most part small, the winds play upon them less boisterously than upon the sea. Lakes and rivers are relatively smooth, and abundantly coated with the membranous film which is a peculiar property of the surface of unruffled water. A diversity of lives is adjusted to this film in but a few fundamentally different ways. A variety of insects have practically the same equipment for skating through life on its upper side. A variety of snails and insect larvae have essentially uniform mechanisms for clinging and crawling on its under side. Many plants like the duck-weed and the water lily live beneath the surface of the water and float their leaves in similar fashion on the film.

Freezing and evaporation are general hazards of living in fresh water against which Nature has provided a general type of protection. The life cycles of most fresh-water creatures include resting stages which are much the same whether they take the form of seed, egg, or chrysalis.

Wells, Huxley, and Wells, in "The Science of Life," cite a remarkable convergent adaptation of this sort. Certain unrelated fresh-water rotifers and crustaceans produce only females during summer. These multiply by virgin birth until fall, when normal males and females make a belated appearance. Before winter brings its gift of death, these normal individuals produce a great many hard-skinned, cold-resisting eggs. Though fertilized in fall the eggs lie under the ice until the following spring, when they give rise to another troop of unsexed females.

This strange and complicated cycle is remarkable not only because it has arisen in species of different blood, but because it has arisen in species whose ancestors resided in the sea. It demonstrates again how living needs are a stronger compulsion than dead traditions, and how a common problem may beget a truer kinship than a common inheritance.

The striking physical differences between standing and running fresh water are reflected in the physique of their inhabitants. The denizens of the former are characterized by indolence, which in certain cases is translated into convergent anatomical terms. The frog, the crocodile, and the hippopotamus, for example, are unrelated excepting in their love of the amenities of sluggish water and in their need for air. With time this need has ceased to be a bother. Lazy floaters for countless generations, all three have grown knobs for lifting their nostrils to the air while the rest of their bodies remains coolly and safely in the water.

Streams, on the other hand, impart their energy to their inhabitants. The shiftless floaters of sea and lake are absent there. Fast water molds the flesh along sterner lines. Like all other environments it promotes certain favorite body styles among its devotees. It flattens and smooths many backboneless animals to a uniform pattern of resistance, and it provides them with the same sort of hooks and suckers for clinging to the rocks. It uniformly stream-lines and muscles its backboned inhabitants for fighting the current more aggressively.

Creatures of the higher land, like creatures elsewhere, have always been most uniformly and conspicuously marked by the most widespread and persistent conditions. Viewed against the background of all the lands during all of their known history, the most significant condition in this con-nection is dearth of moisture. The annual plants of the desert, unlike ancestors and relatives of moister realms, spend most of their lives underground in seeds. They estivate through heat in much the same way that certain animals hibernate through cold. Only during the few wet weeks of spring do they show their faces in bloom. The perennials, too, have their crowded hour of glorious life in spring. Though they do not wither away in summer with the annuals, their real life retires into underground bulbs and fleshy roots when the vernal holiday is over.

More plants than one might suspect, however, stand sturdily enough in the dry desert air throughout the year. Cactus, agave, yucca, mesquite, smoke tree, tamarisk, and many other shrubs and trees have learned to live and even to thrive in the earth's least friendly places. Though varied in origin they are alike in one respect. All have mechanisms for conserving the precious moisture which their roots have been able to suck from the stony ground.

These mechanisms vary in details but they are similar in fundamentals. The central principle in all is the reduction of surfaces from which water might be lost by evaporation. The result is that all desert shrubs and trees have small leaves or no leaves at all, the normal work of leaves being transferred to the less extensive surfaces of trunks and stems.

Nearly all have spines or thorns, an added safeguard for hoarded moisture in a world of thirsty animals.

Desert climates are no more friendly to animals than to plants. Throughout geologic history they have repeatedly descended upon the lands to wither the food and waste the water on which the lives of animals depend. Only those animals that could swiftly make the round of the oases could possibly survive. Creatures as biologically diverse as lizards and dogs, and as geologically distant from one another as dinosaurs and horses, have met the challenge of the desert in the only way it might possibly be met with success.

Their bodies were molded to reduce friction with the medium through which they moved. Legs grew longer, toes grew shorter and tended with time to disappear. Many lizards, dinosaurs, rodents, and the kangaroo, took to running on their hind limbs. In all of them the neck and the fore limbs shortened, the tail lengthened to provide counterpoise. Like automobiles they were similarly styled for similar performance regardless of make. Like automobiles those that failed to conform failed also to survive.

Animals that bury themselves in the earth are as surely shaped by the exigencies of their rôles as are those that run on its surface. Whether snake, lizard, swallow, owl, gopher, badger, rat, or mole, they grow to a single pattern. That pattern requires the degeneration of eyes, ears, and tails, which are superfluous underground. It requires the development of strongly clawed fore limbs, sharp incisor teeth, and tapered snouts, which are needed there. Similarly in caverns which are the terrestrial counterpart of the abyssal sea, animals of varied ancestry grow blind, thin, and pale in the manner of their fellow degenerates of the deep.

Yet another pattern applies to those that climb. Their

chests, hips, and shoulders are strengthened for the endless struggle with gravitation, their hands and feet develop prehensile hooks for clinging to the rocks and trees, their ribs are shaped to support the viscera in any outlandish position. Many different creatures have at various times been modeled in this fashion for a life of acrobatics; certain lizards, sloths, and monkeys with considerable success. More than thirty times in the history of the back-boned animals alone have climbers attempted to fly. The same old story of convergence may be told of the three that succeeded. Though wholly unrelated in blood, the pterosaur, the bird, and the bat all developed the wings, rudder, keel, and hollow air-filled bones which are the indispensable mechanisms of flight.

So endlessly, may examples of the basic patterns of successful living be recorded. The difficulty is not to illustrate them but to explain them.

VI

Most theories of evolution deal with these patterns by the simple expedient of neglecting them. They are concerned primarily with the origin of species, with the diversities rather than the similarities in the living world. As late as the sixth edition of "The Origin of Species," Darwin believed that blood relationship is the major cause of close similarities among plants and animals. Today, however, we know that resemblances which have no basis in blood are common; that in many cases they involve the most essential organs of the creatures that exhibit them.

Insofar as Darwin was aware of such resemblances he attempted to cram them into the frame of his natural selection hypothesis. "I am inclined to think," he wrote in the sixth edition, "that as two men have sometimes independ-

ently of one another hit on the same invention, so . . . it
appears that natural selection, working for the good of
each being, and taking advantage of all favorable variations has produced similar organs, as far as function is concerned." Most of Darwin's successors in the science of
biology have been followers with regard to this particular
tenet of his belief.

A few, however, have demurred. Inasmuch as every
useful variation, according to the doctrine of natural selection, arises by chance from an infinity of possible variations, it is incredible to these skeptics that the same variation should arise in two species of totally different ancestry.
To assume that coincidences of this sort have occurred repeatedly seems to them absurd.

Though they may be willing to admit that variation and
selection played a part in such an evolutionary sequence as
that which led from Eohippus to the horse, they doubt
that these factors alone created the horse. It may be true
that an army of immortal monkeys pounding on typewrit-
ers might ultimately produce all the books in the British
Museum. Some of these books, indeed, would seem to have
been written in that fashion, yet it is a known fact that not
one of them actually was. An average horse is a more
subtle, intricate, and intelligent fabrication than an average book. It may have been made by the monkey of
random variation on the typewriter of mechanical selection, but the skeptic is inclined to suspect that both the
monkey and the typewriter had some help.

One need not be a mathematician to sense the improbability that such a long and logical process should have been
only a succession of fortuitous events. One need not be a
mathematician to sense the far greater improbability that
many grazing contemporaries of the horse should have
evolved through almost precisely the same succession of

fortuitous events. The automobile was not the result of a series of lucky accidents, nor are the similarities between the different makes of automobiles the accidental result of a number of such series of accidents. It is hard to believe that the horse and the other grazing mammals were any more accidental.

The skeptics, in short, may suspect the presence of forces in Nature which have not yet been proved in the laboratory to exist. They may even open their minds to the teleological heresies of the vitalists. Unfortunately these heresies are no more convincing than the orthodox assumptions of the mechanists. Aristotle's "internal perfecting tendency," Schopenhauer's "will," Driesch's "entelechy," Bergson's "élan vital," and a host of other conceptions of a vital force which transcends the known limits of physical and chemical laws, are all unacceptable to the skeptical mind. The assumption of such a force is not explanation but belief, and the belief has been impotent in the scientific attack upon the mysteries of creation.

Where, then, may the scientific skeptic go for light? How may the curious layman who desires to accept the universe know what manner of universe to accept? The answer is all too simple. There is no certain light, no unequivocal universe. There is only the hope that somewhere in the wilderness between the doctrines of chance and design a solution to the enigma of life may someday be discovered.

Pending that discovery there remains the marvelous fitness of creatures for the lives they lead. It is the most striking aspect of vital phenomena. To be sure, there are strange deviations from the general rule, where death rather than life would seem to be the goal of existence. There are moths that destroy themselves in fire and females that devour their young. But these impulses toward death are exceptional. The adaptations of most creatures are for the improvement and prolongation of their lives.

Because adaptation is predominantly beneficial even when it leads to stagnation and degeneracy, because it cleaves to certain definite and stable patterns of success, life may truly be called purposive. Purposive adaptation of structure and behavior is neither sophistry nor myth, but an easily apparent property of living creatures. It is as much a property of flesh as irritability and contractility, as significant in the adjustments of plants and animals as the capacity to eat and to reproduce. It is as much a force as magnetism, electricity, and gravitation—and probably as much a law.

No one can formulate that law in terms of human purpose. No one indeed can state it precisely in any terms. But this is no proof that the law does not exist. The nearly universal spectacle of fitness argues that it must exist. It argues that the doctrine of chance, despite its gain in intellectual respectability since Empedocles first gave it to the world, is yet not the complete and final answer to the riddle of creation.

The tendency to fitness, whatever its motivation, is the rock on which the edifice of life has been built. However strong the winds of chance may blow, the rock remains. Men in the swirl of their lives may feel that the winds blow strong indeed, but the rock is there for men no less than for mice. The successful ones will find it and hold fast.

Chapter IV

THE HOUSE DIVIDED

Despite the inherent tendency toward fitness, there is no royal road to success. Life for all creatures, whatever their lot, is full of sound and fury. Peace is a beautiful concept of the human mind but it is as unusual as it is beautiful. There is no evidence that as a concept it has ever occurred to another mind, or that as a practice it has ever been significantly involved in terrestrial affairs.

For two billion years those affairs have proceeded through conflict. Rivers, wind, and moving ice have worked to tear down the lands; volcanoes and subterranean upheavals have worked to build them up. Never have the titanic conflicts of these forces been much or for long disturbed by peace. The earth as we know it, indeed, would cease to exist if peace as we imagine it should ever truly come. So too with the creatures that live on the earth. Conflict is inherent in their nature.

Ever since Darwin invented the phrase, "the struggle for existence," and Spencer "the survival of the fittest," there has been a general misconception of what these phrases were meant to mean. Their inventors intended them as metaphor. Both Darwin and Spencer knew that there is more in the struggle of creatures to survive than killing one another. They knew that the struggle is not always directly competitive, that it involves a multitude of responses to a multitude of problems. They knew that organisms struggle against every limitation that cramps their lives and not merely against their neighbors.

It requires no special intuition to see that life is not

easy in a lifeless world. The beautiful adjustments of creatures to their physical environments do not fall like manna
from the sky. They are won by endless struggle with the
earth. However unwilled the struggle may be and however arbitrary the outcome, it is still a struggle. It requires
no special intuition to see, on the other hand, that this
struggle with the physical environment is only one phase
of the struggle to live.

With marvelous energy and invention, the living jelly
has pressed to the ends of the earth. Look through the window of Beebe's bathysphere and you see it lighting the
night of the abyss. Look to the sky and you see it again,
racing the wind. Look to the forbidding waters of caves
and hot springs, to the tundras of the north or the deserts
of the south; look even to the pools of petroleum which
have been locked from the air for eons, and life is there.
Look in a million hidden nooks and crannies, for life is
almost everywhere. And wherever you find it you will
find it geared with the nicety of clockwork to the lifeless
world.

Wherever you find it you will find its inventiveness
matched by its fertility. Where one creature may chance
to roam, others are sure to follow. Adjustment to one another is as much a problem of living things as is adjustment to water, air, and rock. Indeed, it is a greater problem
because the prodigal womb of Nature knows no rest. It
always spawns two creatures where only one may grow.
A great misfortune of mice and men is that there are too
many of them.

A great misfortune of most creatures who have thronged
the earth for a billion years is that they were ever born.
Their lives were blessed with no slightest hope of fulfillment, even when fulfillment consisted merely in eating and
avoiding being eaten until reproduction had been achieved.

For Nature ordained that creatures shall be born in vast excess of the space and food which are necessary to sustain them, that consequently most must die before they have well begun to live.

One of the most interesting experiments ever made in the breeding of animals was that of Professor Lorande Loss Woodruff at Yale. Starting with a single microscopic slipper animalcule as founder, Woodruff maintained a pedigreed line of descendants. Reproduction proceeded by simple division of the body without any fanfare of sexuality, at the rate of three generations in two days. At the end of five years some three thousand generations had been evolved. If all the members of all these generations had lived, their flesh would have equalled the volume of ten thousand earths. By the nine thousandth generation the culture would have pushed to the ends of the known universe, outward bound with the speed of light.

A female termite in the fulness of her reproductive stride lays sixty eggs per minute. Without some effective check the world would crawl with termites overnight. The offspring of a single pair of codfish would curdle the seas in a decade. The great-great-grandchildren of one average oyster, if all matured, would number in the neighborhood of ten octillions—enough to make a pile of shells ten thousand times the size of Earth. Fertility is in general inversely proportional to the size of the organism, yet even the modestly breeding and nearly extinct elephants might shortly smother the globe, were their reproductive potentialities to be realized in full.

No such embarrassment is likely to befall the earth because Nature ordained that her children shall be as proficient in murder as in love. Only a few species are at present increasing at all, and many have perished completely in the past. Nature abhors disproportion. She balances the day with the night, birth with death, and fertility with strife. Strife for food, safety, and the chance to reproduce is the kernel of life's adventure.

To suggest the existence of any purpose in the arrangements of Nature is to invite the mechanist's taunt. Yet anyone familiar with the broad outlines of biologic history knows with Tennyson that these arrangements are careless of the single life but extremely careful of the type. There may be no personalized "Nature" with the desire to keep her creation going regardless of the cost to the individuals who compose it, yet that is essentially what has happened, whatever words we select to express it. Nature may not have "meant" that most creatures should live merely to provide food for one another, yet that is all most of them have achieved, whether it was meant or not.

Ever since Malthus and Darwin shook the thinking world with their demonstration of an earth too small and lean to rear all the seed of its loins, the clash of living has been generally assumed to be chiefly the result of overpopulation. But it is easy to demonstrate that overpopulation is only part of the cause for the clash. Even in a far less populous world living would be a hazardous business. Regardless of the number of creatures involved, most organic associations are bound to be felonious because Nature made living synonymous with eating.

Were there but half as many plants and animals in the world, the proportion of robbery and murder would unfortunately be much as it is today. If there were but one lichen, one reindeer, one wolf, and one worm to share all the beauty and bounty of the earth, they would yet be largely devoted to devouring one another. The nutritive chains which bind all living things together and make all living possible also bind all society to a level somewhat lower than Utopia.

II

The technique of conflict at its most merciful is hardly benign. At its most cruel it is far more terrible than mere murder for self-preservation. There is the familiar example of the cat who is not content to kill the mouse for nourishment but must also torture it for fun. There are the young whelks who are born in sealed capsules where their only possible food is one another. There are the solitary bee-killing wasps who kill their victims for the few drops of honey in their crops.

Such horrible expedients are disgusting to men and more than one man has said so. Nature for William James was a harlot to whom we owe no moral allegiance and with whom as a whole we can establish no moral communion. Even John Burroughs who loved the harlot for her virtues felt only sadness for her faults. "What savagery," he wrote, "what thwartings and delays, what carnage and suffering, what an absence of all that we mean by intelligent planning and oversight. . . . Just a clash of forces, the battle to the strong and the race to the fleet."

Happily such effusions rise less in the facts of Nature than in the moods of men. Part of the frailty of man is to see all natural phenomena in the light of his own sensibilities. But even by human standards the laws that govern the phenomena are not invariably cruel. Even in the relationships of creatures to one another there is balm for the tender-minded. In the lush fulness of her harlotry, Nature embraces many things. She embraces love as well as hunger, the love of mate for mate and of mates for offspring. She embraces coöperation as well as conflict, conjugal in the nest and communal in the herd. She embraces loyalty as well as treason, loyalty of individuals to their generation and of generations to their race. She does all this in the self-conscious sight of man. What she does in the sight of the Absolute is less easy to say.

One thing, however, is clear. Just as there have been but few fundamentally different plots in the history of drama so also have there been but few fundamentally different rôles. In the drama of life the sun is the protagonist without which there could be no action. Next in importance are the green plants which alone are able to shape the sun's energy to the purposes of the play, and the colorless plants, especially the bacteria, which help keep the plot a-boiling. Then there are the herbivorous animals that eat the plants, the carnivores that eat the herbivores, the saprophytes and scavengers that eat the remains of both. Though countless minor rôles have from time to time been added, these are the only invariable and important ones.

There are too many actors in the drama of life to permit any strictly non-competitive rôles, but in some rôles the competition is as impersonal and clean as a man could reasonably desire. The lives of green plants, for example, are enviably moral. They feed for the most part on materials that do not enlist the sentiments and they breed without ecstasy or remorse. They vie politely with one another for sun and air, and they make the world beautiful as well as habitable for the rest of creation.

It does not follow, however, that existence for them is a sinecure. The entire vast and intricate web of life is anchored in the ability of the green plants to wrest sugar from the lifeless elements. Theirs is the task of grappling directly with the unvarnished crudities of the world. When water, light, and heat withhold their largess or too prodigally bestow it, they cannot run away with the animals to fairer lands. Because only their seeds are normally motile, they advance towards safety from generation to generation slowly like a man who is paralyzed by fear in a dream. More squarely than any other creatures they must face the music of a violent and fickle world, however loud and unlovely it may be. More faithfully than any other creatures they transcribe into their lives the restless rhythms of that world.

Though the struggles of green plants are largely against the indifferent hostilities of their physical environment they are far from being wholly so. Green plants like all other creatures must suffer the embarrassment of being too many. The earth is rich in the simple substances that are necessary to sustain their lives, but it is not nearly so rich as their fertility.

Their rivalry is no less genuine for being gentle. It is most severe among plants that are most alike in their needs. On the washes of the Colorado Desert, the creosote bushes are spaced at remarkably regular intervals, each bush commanding all the sparse bounty of a definite area. For each bush that gains the means of survival in this dour land, many less fortunate ones must die. In the lusher woodlands of the North, countless seedlings are born that can never mature. With time the weaker are robbed of moisture, light, and air, by the stronger of their kind. To make a forest, many are called but few are chosen.

Similarly on the tundras of the arctic, moss vies with moss for foothold on the barren ground, and the mosses with the lichens. On the mountains and moorlands of Britain, fern battles fern, and the ferns the grasses. Though no emotion or blood is spent in the process the lucky and the strong of the vegetable world have everywhere and always lived at the expense of the luckless and the weak.

In some instances green plants seek fancier food than the gases, salts, and liquors of air and earth. Certain moors

and marshes are so lean in these simple essentials of a normal vegetable existence as to have engendered queer tastes
among some of their inhabitants. Venus' flytrap, for example, is a plant with such a strange appetite that Linnaeus
dubbed it *miraculum Naturae*.

The gaily tinted leaves of this plant form a flat rosette
from the center of which a stalk of flowers rises. Each
leaf is a trap consisting of a two-lobed blade whose lobes
are movable on one another. The margins of each blade
are studded with long stiff interlocking spines. In the middle of the blades are bristles which when stroked cause the
trap to shut its mouth. The flytrap, in short, is a plant whose
beauty is deceit and whose food is flesh.

When an insect in its innocence brushes the bristles it
finds death embedded in nectar. By a device which is a
vegetable version of muscle it is caught in a prison which
is a vegetable version of a stomach. The rose-colored
patches then show their truer colors. They are glands that
secrete a ferment which both tightens the jaws of the trap
and digests its content. After a week or so when the meal
is absorbed the jaws relax for another feeding.

The marvel of this plant is the mechanism of its adaptation to the life of a beast of prey. Like other green plants
it is basically designed for gaseous and liquid food. Super-
imposed upon this design is a mammal-like mechanism for
handling solid food. No organisms are less alike in origin
than flowering plants and mammals. The mechanism which
makes the flytrap a mammal in function is one of the most
marvelous examples of convergence in the world. It is also
one of the strangest freaks in the world. The business of
green plants is to produce organic compounds and not to
purloin them. Animals—who cannot produce enough of
these commodities for their needs—are more properly the
thieves.

III

Life is a conflagration that would soon be smothered in its ashes were the ashes not carried away. Just as the green plants stoke the furnace of life with sugar, the colorless plants remove the ashes through decay. To be sure, the colorless plants do not perform this necessary housework of the world alone, but they do by far the greatest share of it. That they do it well is evidenced by the fact that the débris of death has never become a conspicuous or an embarrassing burden upon life.

The colorless plants not only remove the clutter of death but they shape it to the usages of life. Without their ministrations life would soon be not only suffocated but exhausted. The riches won from the lifeless world would return to the lifeless world, and so very shortly would life itself. By reminting the worn-out coins of mortality, the colorless plants produce a currency of immortality.

The creatures that perform this invaluable service are not admirable by any ordinary human standard of virtue, nor are their functions attractive by any ordinary human standard of beauty. Decay by ordinary standards is the filthy business of loathsome creatures. Furthermore, a few of these creatures are known to suffer a sort of impatience which impels them to work on neighbors who are not yet entirely dead, and this does not raise the status of their kind in the estimation of man. Inasmuch as man is sometimes the victim of their impatience, his opinion is not wholly unreasonable. For the most part, however, the colorless plants are helpful to man. They bring him tuberculosis and pneumonia, but they also help him raise his food and later digest it.

Their attitude toward man and toward life in general, however, is neither aesthetic nor moral. It was their fate to lose their green color during the course of evolution, and with it their ability to live on the lifeless elements. Denied the life of orthodox plants, they are forced to live like animals. In view of this fact it is not remarkable that a few of them embarrass the animals, but rather that so few of them do. By far the greatest number of them are content to live on food and in places that most other creatures disdain.

A wood is the best place to see these master undertakers of the world at work. The litter of dead vegetation beneath the trees is really a theater teeming with life. Beetles, worms, and insect grubs grow fat there on the liquors of decay, and so in much greater number and variety do toadstools, mushrooms, yeasts, and molds. But one does not see the most abundant and significant organisms of the forest floor. The bacteria, invisible to the naked eye, do most of the work in that busy realm, and could easily do all if their colleagues should ever desert them.

Because of the physiologic diversity of these simple plants, they are the supreme masters in the art of preparing the dead to live again. Certain putrefying bacteria specialize in converting the defunct protoplasm of fallen plants and animals into water, carbon dioxide, and hydrogen sulphide. Certain others attack the nitrogenous molecules of fat and protein and turn them into ammonium carbonate. Others make nitrites of the ammonium carbonate and still others make nitrates of the nitrites. In the end the complex substances of protoplasm are reduced to simple compounds and gases which the green plants can utilize as food. The precious elements, especially the carbon, which organisms have won from the mineral world, are put back into circulation in the living world.

The theater of bacterial activity lies below the threshold of ordinary observation. Even when helped by the microscope, men see only a small part of the drama that is being enacted there, and understand only a small part of what they see. They know, however, that neither the tastes nor the scruples of the actors are high, and that from the humane point of view the drama is violent and cruel. Like bands of rival gangsters the bacteria fight for the unsavory spoils of death, which despite their melancholy abundance are yet not sufficiently abundant to glut the hunger of all. But men also know that whatever the bacteria may be in the lesser drama of their private lives, in the greater drama of Life they are not villains but heroes.

IV

Between the green plants and the scavengers are the hordes of creatures that must kill to live. No amount of whitewash can obscure the fact that the theme of their lives is war. Just as in love by the old adage there is one who loves and one who is loved, in war it may be said that there is one who attacks and one who resists. Offense and defense are essential ingredients of conflict; do away with either and conflict must end. When Nature arranged that war should be a basic principle in the economy of the living world, she arranged that the two techniques should be intricately intermingled. She arranged that life should consist very largely in the practice of both techniques, that it should be half a war of offense for food and half a war of defense against being reduced to food. The green plants and the scavengers alone have achieved neutrality, the first by giving the belligerents what they want and the second by taking only what they want no longer.

The chains of hostilities that stretch from the green plants to the scavenging animals do not readily yield to a simplified analysis. They can be assayed, however, in a general way with reference to their essential ingredients. Though all the warriors must possess a certain minimum ability in both techniques of war, some of them tend to specialize in the one technique and some of them in the other. These preferences in fighting coincide in many cases with preferences in food.

Just as the need to eat creates the need to fight, the kind of feeding determines the kind of fighting. And just as fighting can be roughly classified as offensive and defensive, feeding can be roughly classified as carnivorous and herbivorous. Many animals, to be sure, eat flesh and vegetation with equal delight, but many others are strongly prejudiced in favor of one or the other. The specialists in meat are inclined to be specialists in offense, the specialists in plants are inclined to be specialists in defense. The first operate on the principle that the best defense is a good offense, and the second reverse the formula.

Inasmuch as the plants put up no real defense against the plant-eating animals, it can hardly be held that the plant-eating animals conduct any real offensive against the plants. The nutritional problem of the herbivores is not conquest but exploitation, and their equipment consists not of weapons but of tools. The problem, for all that, is still a problem. Nature, astringent even in her generosities, created the dilemma of Tantalus long before she created the Greeks. She supplied the herbivores with abundant food but also with abundant obstacles to its utilization. She arranged that the plants should not surrender their energies as meekly as they surrender their persons.

Whether in the sea or on the land, only those animals succeed in the herbivorous life that possess an adequate apparatus for gathering and milling large quantities of vegetation. Even the most efficient of them can wring out but little of the energy which is locked up in the food they eat.

They have little time as a result for anything but eating. A cow munching grass from dawn to dusk symbolizes the lives of them all.

The security of the cow's harem existence, however, extends no farther than the pasture fence. Her fellows of the wild are in daily danger of death. Unlike the carnivores who do most of death's work among them, most herbivores are unable to use their organs of nutrition as organs of protection. Those plant-eating species that have best succeeded in life through the ages have possessed other means to this end. Some have been armored to withstand their enemies, some disguised to deceive them. Some have eluded them by burrowing, some by swimming or running away. But all have been specialists of one sort or another in defense. Through the ages defense has been their major method of offense against the carnivores, and their continued prosperity proves that the method works.

The continued prosperity of the carnivores, on the other hand, proves that their method also works. Long before wolves took to hunting horses on the plains, trilobites took to hunting brachiopods in the seas. Far back in the Ordovician period when many marine creatures had developed hard limy shells, many others had developed sharp jaws for cracking them. And from that time on, the mechanisms of offense have kept pace with the mechanisms of defense. The forceps of crustaceans, the stings of jellyfishes, the beaks of squids, the teeth of sharks, the poisons of spiders and snakes, the fangs and claws of weasels and tigers, are but a few of the devices which have appeared through the ages to further that end.

At first thought it might seem that the beasts of prey have the greater advantage in the struggle for survival. But to study their history as it is revealed, for example, among the dinosaurs of the Mesozoic era is to question this assumption. Pacifists have made parables about those ancient reptilian rulers. The bloody-toothed dinosaurs, they say, were the strongest warriors the world has ever known, yet all of them are dead. The aggressive way of life is accordingly foredoomed to failure.

But these pacifists do not mention the logical corollary of their argument. They overlook the fact that by similar reasoning the defensive way of life is likewise foredoomed to failure. For the gentle plant-eating dinosaurs are also undeniably dead. The truth is that the herbivorous and the carnivorous dinosaurs were equally successful when the star of the dinosaurs was high, and equally unfortunate when it set. The two lived together in an essentially balanced society for one hundred and fifty million years. Extinction eventually came to both chiefly because of their inability to adjust themselves to a profoundly altered physical environment. Races like men are punished for their ineptitudes without reference to their virtues or their sins.

Our present interest, however, is not in the disappearance but in the continuance of races. How has the house of life been able to stand for a billion years so murderously divided against itself?

V

The lives that each day go down the collective gullet of the animal kingdom are beyond computation. A few species, to be sure, are peculiarly abstemious. A twenty-foot python can manage on less than a pound of meat per foot per week, but he is decidedly an exception. Most animals are incorrigible gluttons. An ordinary caterpillar eats twice its own weight daily. The hummingbird, whose beauty stops short of the spiritual, consumes relatively as much. But the record goes to the grub that was observed to eat about 86,000 times its initial weight before settling down to pupate into a moth.

Because their food is highly concentrated, the meat-eaters must defer to the plant-eaters in such record individual performances at table. Their group performances, however, are impressive, as may be shown by a quantitative estimate of the links in the chain which leads to a pound of codfish. Ten pounds of sea snails must be eaten by a cod to make that pound of codfish. Each pound of snails in turn is the product of ten pounds of worms, and each pound of worms the product of ten pounds of microscopic organisms. Before the codfish can appear on a platter, half a ton of living flesh must be destroyed.

Such a nutritive sequence illustrates not only how murderous the business of existence is, but also, paradoxically, how that business can succeed in spite of its being so. With the sole exception of modern man, every animal that ever lived has occupied its appropriate niche or niches in one or more of these sequences. Food chains are the economic framework of society at large. However defective they may be morally, mechanically they are almost perfect. They have prevented society these many eons from tearing itself to pieces.

All animals exist in a deluge of physical, chemical, and biological influences, but no two species make precisely the same adjustments to precisely the same storm. Two adjustments of a general nature, however, are mandatory upon all. All animals (again with the exception of modern man) must adjust themselves to a supply of food, on the one hand, and to a supply of enemies on the other. Through the establishment of these two relationships the links in the food chains are forged.

A common characteristic of these chains is that the links increase consecutively in size. The size of an animal's food, in other words, is apt to be a little smaller than the animal, and his enemies are apt to be a little larger. Certain obvious exceptions to this rule come easily to mind. Most plant-eating animals are not inhibited by food which is larger than themselves. Plants are notoriously weak in reprisal and slow in retreat, and animals are notoriously devoid of a sense of sin. Excepting such fastidious specialists as the seed-eating birds and the honey-sucking insects, the smallest herbivores will attack the largest trees with impunity.

Certain carnivores, too, may take on adversaries larger than themselves, but like the herbivores they do so only because they are reasonably certain of success. In every known case of this sort there is some special adaptation which gives the smaller, animal the advantage. Thus it is that snakes and weasels, who can paralyze their prey with poison and fright, respectively, can also be smaller than their prey without much danger to themselves. Other animals increase their effective size by hunting in groups. Predatory bands of such small animals as the driver ants of Africa and the tigerfish of the Amazon can master opponents many times larger than their individual selves.

Just as a few animals step upward towards food which is considerably larger than themselves, a few step downward towards food which is considerably smaller. The corpulent whale-bone whale, for example, subsists on crustaceans that are almost too small to be seen. But just as stepping far upward normally increases the risk of violent death, stepping far downward normally increases the risk of starvation. Excepting at the surface of the sea, excessively small food is only periodically available to the larger animals. Most of them, accordingly, are restricted to food which is just slightly smaller than themselves.

The fundamental principle of the food chain is to make food available progressively from the smaller to the larger

animals. By the testimony of many field naturalists the principle is widely enforced. C. D. H. Carpenter, who studied
the tsetse fly of Africa, has furnished an example which
proves that it may also be rigidly enforced. Tsetse flies can
suck the blood of the mammals but not of the lungfishes in
their Lake Victoria kingdom. The corpuscles of the one
are just small enough to pass up the proboscis of the insect,
and the corpuscles of the other are just large enough to
get stuck. A few millionths of a meter, accordingly, is
just enough to hold the dread carriers of sleeping sickness
from a tasty addition to their diet. The same few millionths of a millimeter is just enough to keep the most
gluttonous mammal in the world from some 30,000 square
miles of rich and desirable land.

Gradation in size is only half the requirement for a food
chain. Gradation in number is the other half. The chain
that led to the pound of codfish consisted of creatures that
were progressively larger in size and at the same time progressively fewer in number. This is the normal condition
throughout the living world. Unless the number of creatures decreases as their size increases, their food chains
must collapse.

There must be, for example, fewer foxes than rabbits
in a given region as long as the former depend on the latter
for food. Should the reverse come to pass, the rabbits
would disappear by murder. Unless they could find other
suitable food, the foxes would disappear by starvation or
migration. In any event the rabbit-fox food chain of the
region would be destroyed. Such things are known to
have happened but they are relatively rare. Nature normally preserves a balance between the rapacity and the
fertility of her children.

A mountain lion in Montana may kill as many as fifty
deer in a winter, yet only where men have interfered are

lions notably increasing or deer decreasing. Nature has balanced the fertility of the deer against the rapacity of the
lions so that both species may continue to exist. Similarly,
an owl in exercising the prerogatives of owlhood destroys
several smaller birds; which in their turn eat thousands of
spiders, worms, and insects; which consume untold millions
of other creatures lesser than themselves.

So it is that though the lion and the lamb do not lie down
together in peace, they live together in an essentially balanced society. Everywhere in chains of varying length do
the larger, stronger, and fewer live at the expense of the
smaller, weaker, and more abundant. Each species pays
the price of existence with the surplus of individuals which
Nature has provided for that purpose, but retains a modest
balance in the bank with which to carry on.

We thus arrive at a strange and embarrassing conclusion.
The reproductive powers being what they are, it is impossible to imagine a well adjusted society of animals without
conflict. Without enemies to whittle down its numbers to
the measure of its food supply, many a species would breed
itself into the grave. The house of life divided against itself
stands only because it is divided!

The dire effects of losing one's enemies were recently
demonstrated by the deer of the Kaibab National Forest
in Arizona. The tender-hearted tenders of the forest in
Washington sent specialists to destroy the cougars. Freed
of this embarrassment, the deer multiplied luxuriantly until
they were cropping all the edible vegetation in the forest
before the snows set in. As the snow grew deeper the deer
grew thinner, and gathered around the houses of ranchers
to beg for food. Before this finest herd of deer in the
country· was destroyed by its own fertility, the guardians
in Washington let loose on them an enemy quite as effective

as the original cougars. They opened the forest to hunters. Very soon thereafter the herd was reduced to a size commensurate with survival.

If what happened to this food chain in an Arizona preserve should happen simultaneously to all the food chains in the world, society would collapse. Fortunately, the Guardian of this larger preserve is not apt to make such a mistake. He will doubtless continue to protect the order of the world through war, and the welfare of the species through an appropriate quota of enemies.

Pacifists, however, have no cause to shudder nor militarists to chuckle at these facts. Though wars between such creatures as termites and ants are sufficiently well organized and bloody to suggest the wars between men, they are different in one significant respect. They are wars between members of different species. With but a few exceptions, the wars of animals in general are fought between creatures belonging to different species.

It is true, of course, that individuals of the same species (who share the same environment and require the same kind of food and mates) may quarrel bitterly with one another. The fisherman knows that a pike will rise to a baby pike as readily as to a shiner. The lobster culturist knows that lobsters prefer lobster to any other food. The paleontologist knows that the wounds in the skulls of the great horned dinosaurs were made by the horns of other horned dinosaurs. Everywhere and always brothers have clutched at each other's throat.

Such conflicts, however, are comparable to the so-called peacetime activities of men, to the endless rub of business, mating, and crime. They are individual rather than collective phenomena. When death results it is comparable to homicide rather than to human warfare. Men are practically alone in the living world in being chronically addicted to both individual and group murder among themselves.

VI

The evolution of man was not a wholly triumphant march toward bliss. Like the evolution of every other creature it entailed losses as well as gains. Gaining fire, clothing, and cod-liver oil, man lost much of his natural resistance to cold. Gaining cookery and a variety of gastric delights, he lost much of his natural aptitude for digestion. Gaining an elaborate system of defense, he lost many of his natural enemies. Of all his losses he regrets the last one least though he suffers for it most. Unlike the deer that suffered a similar loss, man has no prospect of enjoying an easy cure.

When man shifted the burden of locomotion from hands to feet he took the most decisive step in his evolution. Not until his hands were free could they free in turn the latent ingenuity of his brain. The material culture which distinguishes him from other creatures began with the first human hand to strike sparks from a stone. His social economy which is equally distinctive began with the first human hand to throw the stone at an enemy. This ability to throw a missile led to bullets in a negligible fraction of geologic time, and so to the loss of enemies that had faithfully served the ancestors of men for millions of years.

When man labeled the lion the king of beasts he indulged in such chivalry as a real king can easily afford. For however kingly a lion may seem to a gazelle, he is only an easy target for a rifle. Few animals have a chance against the weapons of modern man, and few are so stupid or uninformed as not to act in accordance. Only in occasional nightmares do civilized men encounter the enemies that their forbears faced daily in the flesh.

Even in India where animals still dare to compete with men, the casualties of the latter as listed by the Home Department are far fewer than those of the former. Nor can the insects that conduct an occasional foray across the fences of civilization consolidate their gains. Even the potent armies of infection are steadily losing ground. Men die to an ever increasing extent from their own private ailments without any help from germs.

Man, in fact, has so thoroughly eliminated or subdued all serious competitors in the living world that he thinks of himself as akin to the mighty forces of the physical world. If the truth were spoken, he thinks of himself as the ruler of these forces, and of his evolution as a movement toward that end. In view of this attitude his indifference to certain matters of merely biological importance can be understood. Yet because of this indifference and despite his triumphs he has become the unhappiest species on earth.

The elimination of enemies was the first and most fundamental step in this direction. Few men would see anything but evil in enemies and anything but good in their abolition. This is the civilized view. Insofar as men can agree on anything it is that life should be safe and soft, and few would deny that the elimination of enemies has helped to make it so. History shows, however, that though the elimination of enemies has furthered the softening of human life, it has done the opposite for its safety.

For a billion years the economy of the living world had been based on the principle that the fertility of flesh shall balance its rapacity. Any system that had worked so effectively for so long a time could hardly have been without merit. Its merit, however, was not such as to appeal to so strangely moral and aesthetic a creature as man. Its strength was not such as to hold so restless and resourceful a creature against his will. A lover of new deals from the beginning, man abandoned a social economy that had worked for a billion years in favor of one that has not worked at all.

Capitalistic imperialism is commonly credited with this achievement but its roots go very much deeper than that. They go down to man's earliest mammalian ancestors. Judged by their teeth which have survived them, those arboreal brutes were not fussy about their food. They avoided the prejudices of such narrow-minded feeders as tigers and cows. They apparently lived on insects when they could catch them, and on nuts, fruits and leaves when they could not. Those of their descendants that led to man were presumably not any fussier because man is the most versatile feeder that ever lived.

The full flower of this versatility could not appear until sometime after the human hand was free. When the ancestors of man swung down from the trees, they entered a region of new delights which was also a region of new dangers. They had to perfect their cunning before they could indulge their cupidity. Until clubs and stones were conscripted to the support of muscles and teeth, man had to be content with discretion as a policy, and with his more gentle neighbors as food.

Through the perfection of hand-wielded weapons and tools, man was able to throw off these restrictions. He greatly increased the size of his food by adding large animals to his diet. With the domestication of grain he added seeds, a food much smaller than any he had been able to rely on before. He thus became the first species capable of using food of practically all sizes and varieties, the first to throw off completely the ancient shackles of the food chain. He became the first species with a prospect of enjoying its food in peace, free both from annoying competitors and dangerous foes. He became the first species that might lift its thoughts from the stomach to the stars. But he also became a freak.

He became an omnivorous creature with the blended instincts of lion and lamb, but without the checks that Nature normally imposes upon these instincts. As a lamb he lacked the outer check of enemies, and as a lion the inner check of relative infertility. He became simultaneously the fiercest and most prolific creature on earth. Unlike the deer of the Kaibab Forest he had no Guardian to balance his biologic budget. He, accordingly, balanced it himself by setting his own rapacity against his own fecundity. He became the enemy of himself. Compared in malignity with this newer foe, his older foes were friends.

It is a perennially popular belief among men that war in von Moltke's famous phrase is "part of God's world order," the price men pay for having been descended from beasts. The belief is not without a certain practical worth. It affords a spurious justification for the few who profit by war and a spurious nobility for the many who lose. But the truth is that war as men wage it is the price they pay for being human. It is the tax levied by the criminal and the weak on the decent and the strong. It is the ironic cost of compassion.

It is, in short, the penalty for disobeying the law of natural selection. Man is the only species that lacks a mechanism for eliminating the habitually anti-social and the congenitally weak. He is the only species that can deliberately cherish and promote its own deterioration. He is the only species that is driven by the hot cruelty of sentimentality and the cold cruelty of greed into war upon itself.

Mass murder of men by men is strictly man's own invention. Unlike the interspecific warfare of all other species it prevents rather than preserves an equilibrium of an-

tagonistic forces. It is a cultural disease rather than a biological necessity and it has no value for the species at large.
It has, however, inestimable value for dictators, profiteers
and fools. Through them mankind has been able to make
its unique contribution to the social economy of the living
world.

Chapter V

LIFE WITHOUT STRUGGLE

"F ORCE and fraud," said Thomas Hobbes, "are in war the cardinal virtues." Biologic science three hundred years later discards Hobbes's phrasing but retains his thought. Force and fraud are cardinal aspects of the warfare of living whether dressed in the quaint terminology of human ethics or not. Remove the "force" of predacity and the "fraud" of parasitism from the spectacle and the spectacle disappears.

Life to a considerable extent is the clash of steel on steel, the endless attrition which endless nutrition demands. Organic associations, however, are not invariably antagonistic. Nature, indeed, has provided that the intraspecific relationships of living creatures shall be abundantly coöperative. She has even provided that certain interspecific relationships shall be mutually beneficial, or at least no threat to the welfare of the parties involved. She has also provided that a great many relationships shall be neither deadly nor benign, but corrupt.

Partnership is an ancient but not generally an honorable institution. Though it usually ends in grief for one of the partners, it continues to flourish. It is not surprising that creatures in an overpopulated world should pool their strength in the advance toward a common objective. Nor is it surprising in a world where the sense of fairness very rarely becomes an obsession that those who happen to gain the greater benefits from partnership should accept them without compunction. The remarkable fact is that certain partnerships have not only not occasioned the degradation of one or the other of the parties involved, but have actually insured nearly equal benefits for both.

Those who seek examples of Christian morality in Nature have made a parable of the pilot fish and the shark. To pay for the crumbs which he filches from the latter's feeding, the former is supposed to lead the way to each new meal. Unhappily for the sentiment of the parable many a shark does very well without this alleged service. Indeed, just to look at a shark is to convince oneself that here, if anywhere in the world, is a creature adequate to its calling.

A better example of a mutually beneficial association is the rhinoceros and the birds that dig the ticks from his hide. The rhinoceros gains not only relief from his torment, but also a more reliable warning of danger from his fluttery companions than he could obtain through his own unaided wits. The birds in their turn get only the ticks, but they seem content. So, too, would seem to be the plover which, according to Herodotus, removes leeches from the back of the crocodile and even obligingly picks his teeth.

Perhaps the best instance of a beneficent external partnership is that of the hermit crab and the hydroid. By covering the crab with its fuzzy tentaculated body, the hydroid contributes a disguise as well as a battery of stinging cells when the disguise fails. In return it gains free transportation and scraps from the crustacean's table.

The most intimate beneficent partnerships in Nature are internal rather than external, and so close in some cases that death alone can sunder them. Certain one-celled plants are known to live in such a union with certain one-celled animals. The plant uses the carbon dioxide and the nitrogenous waste produced in the body of the animal, and the animal uses the oxygen and starch produced in the body of the plant. Somewhat similar is the association of a green alga

and a colorless fungus in a lichen. Thus by a strange perversity, creatures with antagonistic feeding habits become
mutually beneficial.

A great many organic associations are helpful only to one
of the members, and yet not harmful to the other. A lichen
clinging to the bark of a tree takes less from the tree than
does the bird that flits among its branches. For the bird
may filch both board and lodging, whereas the lichen is
content with lodging alone. Most of the primitive plants
and animals that infest the mouth and intestines of man live
amicably enough with their overgrown ally. They pasture
on his warm and fertile innards as cows on grass. Many of
them are poachers that make no return for favors received,
but neither do they do any harm.

Similarly, the little fish who dwells unembarrassed in
the rectum of a sea cucumber is a squatter but not a rascal.
Nature, noted neither for justice nor fastidiousness, has
vouchsafed in this instance certain concessions to propriety.
She has shifted the vent of the fish to a spot beneath the
throat, so that when the creature rests with its head pro-
jecting over the threshhold of its strange home it may void
waste without befouling its partner.

Relationships such as these are benign enough but they
are only a step from felony. The strongest impulse in the
living world is the urge to live as easily as possible. Partnership is only a convenience to that end. When convenience
is better served by one partner's taking an unfair advantage
of the other, he takes it. And unless he belongs to a single
species of large-brained, thin-haired mammals, he does so
with neither qualm nor rationalization.

Because everything in Nature merges with something
else, it is not easy to place strict limits upon the definition
of anything. Most biologists are agreed that parasitism is
a one-sided nutritional relationship between two organisms,

which leads to the injury of one and the degeneracy of the other. Some authorities would restrict parasitism to partnerships where one partner has escaped the need of any strenuous struggling to maintain himself. But even so restricted, alas, the ranks of parasitism are full. Half of all the animals alive today are enrolled.

The coyote who sinks his teeth in a rabbit is not a degenerate. He is acting in accordance with the best traditions of his race. Similarly, many germs that are associated with diseases in other creatures are active, and in no sense degenerate organisms. Both are beasts of prey, one working from without, the other from within.

The fly that laps up the sweat of a horse is perhaps more a scavenger than a parasite. The flea that wanders over the belly of a dog, refreshing itself with an occasional nip of blood, is perhaps more a predator than a parasite. But many insects that hypodermatically inject their eggs in the flesh of their neighbors are true parasites, even though their young leave the host when their larval life is over. During their occupancy they steal enough of their victim's fat, with sufficiently little hardship or danger to themselves, to justify the appellation.

Such parasites, however, are among the more respectable of their kind because they periodically abandon their victims. Others, though perennial afflictions to their hosts, have the grace to maraud with some restraint. In the latter group is the mistletoe which takes water and salt from the tree it infests, but uses its own green leaves to manufacture organic food.

Villains of different stripe are the trichina worms which encyst themselves in the muscles of their victims, and which may pass from host to host and from generation to generation without seeing the light of day for years on end. When their host is eaten by another animal, the stomach juices of the latter dissolve the cysts and liberate hordes of worms which pair and bring forth myriads more. One infected pork sandwich can fill a man with as many worms and worries as there are people and problems in the United States. Compared with such villains a parasite as mild and moderate as the mistletoe is only a superfluous decoration.

Trichina is not the only worm that devotes itself to its comrades while they are yet alive. Perhaps the most perfectly adjusted of all parasites is the tapeworm. He has lost his power of locomotion, his sense organs, and his honor; but he has gained a marvelous aptitude for clinging to intestines without being dissolved by their juices, and a prodigious ability in eating and spawning. The tapeworms that inhabit man are so rigidly specialized that they cannot be persuaded to reside in any other creature. Not all parasites, however, are as partial to a given host. The tubercle bacilli, for example, are unhappily quite adaptable.

In some cases parasitism achieves the complexity of a Chinese puzzle. A certain type of caterpillar devotes its life to despoiling the trees of New England. Twenty-three other varieties of insects reside either in or on the caterpillar, and despoil him while he labors. These support thirteen parasites of their own, which in turn harbor two, possibly five, more. One of the last may in some cases be parasitic on another in its own category, thus adding a fourth link to the fantastic chain.

Nature's mind like her womb is fertile. The methods whereby her children victimize one another are, like the children, wondrously diverse. Not only do animals parasitize other animals and plants other plants, but animals parasitize plants and plants animals. Occasionally males even parasitize their own females, as in the case of the seagoing worm *Bonellia* who lives in the oviduct of his spouse.

Some parasites are honest during part of their lives, and others never; some are not particular in the choice of hosts, others specialize on certain hosts or certain successions of hosts; some attack the outside of their victims while others work from the inside.

II

Some years ago the cosmogonist Moore gave a name to a phenomenon which any naturalist willing to lift his eyes from the minutiae of his immediate interests may observe. That phenomenon is the well-nigh universal tendency of matter and energy to assume the most complicated possible forms. It is Moore's belief—and the belief of many other astronomers and chemists—that the materials in a cooling globe grow gradually more complex; that atoms, molecules, oxides, carbonates, colloids, and living protoplasm itself, represent successive responses to the gradual reduction of temperature. Moore labeled this tendency the Law of Complexity, "a law universal in its application to all matter, although varying in intensity in different types of matter, and holding throughout all space as generally as the law of gravitation."

One, indeed, need not look to the distant stars for evidence of its operation. The stream that started as a rill and a handful of sand to end as a hundred-headed Amazon with the bones of mountains in its maws; the sensitivity that began in the placid polyps of the past to arrive eventually at the troubled spirit of man; the individual creatures that originated in little blobs of jelly and grew into Shakespeare, Michelangelo, and Christ—these and many lesser marvels of the earth exemplify the Law of Complexity.

In looking at the elaborate web of organic associations one wonders if it too may not illustrate the law; whether it too may not once have been more simple. One wonders if the varieties of social relationships, which range through a multitude of gradations from the benign to the malignant, may not have arisen in some such order through time; if in the very beginning all creatures may not have shifted for themselves.

Because of the dearth and imperfection of fossils in the oldest rocks, these questions will perhaps never be conclusively answered. Unicellular organisms today swarm in the flesh of their larger neighbors like motes in a shaft of light. It is difficult to believe and impossible to prove that they did not always do so. The union of bacteria and protozoans with the tissues of higher plants and animals is a universal phenomenon, an integral part of the chemistry of life as far as we are permitted to know it. The more mechanical associations of many-celled creatures with each other, on the contrary, are clearly acquired rather than fundamental characteristics. Despite the mutilated evidence of the rocks, such associations have an evolutionary history which may be read.

In the Cambrian period when life first recorded its adventuring in any fulness, some ninety percent of the animals known from fossils lived remarkably active and independent lives. Though life had perhaps even then existed for half a billion years, it had not yet been greatly debased by torpor. Few sluggards sagged under the weight of their shells, or rooted themselves in the mud. And completely absent were any of the intimacies that mark and so widely mar society today.

Though records are faulty, there is no doubt that lethargy spread in the ranks of the living with the passage of Paleozoic time; that partnerships were conceived and nourished by the growing urge to live as comfortably and easily as possible; that with such motivation the unhappy institution of parasitism was inevitable. There is no pat proof of this genesis for every known instance of parastic degeneracy, but there is sufficient proof to render the assumption reasonable enough.

Both because of their services to the dead and their disservices to the living, worms have never been popular with men. But they are the darlings of the gods, and biologically as admirable and successful a group of organisms as ever existed. Nature, in fact, would seem to have been especially pleased when she hit upon the bilaterally symmetrical plan of a worm. She made it the model for all her higher creation. She altered it diversely in the bodies of crabs and men but she never entirely abandoned it. She retained it in a multitude of lesser deviations from its pristine simplicity in the worms themselves, from the dawn of Pre-Cambrian time to the noon of today.

Inasmuch as worms have been quite generally free from the burden of cumbrous skeletons, their record in the rocks must be vastly disproportionate to their ancient number and importance. Many were doubtless decent members of society in the past as are many of their tribe today. But unfortunately for their reputation as a group, worms have ever been cursed by a sizeable percentage of blackguards who press their advantages without counting the cost to others. Fortunately for the history of parasitic degeneration, worms of this type have been more abundantly preserved as fossils than have their more honest relatives.

The earliest worms were recorded only in trails and burrows in the soft sea mud. Later some of them built calcareous tubes into which they withdrew when danger threatened, and from which they forayed when the omens were auspicious. Such tubes are found in association with the shells of other creatures in rocks as old as Silurian, and the associations increase in complexity in successively younger formations.

In the Silurian and early Devonian periods, the tube-dwelling worms began to show an attachment for corals which they have never since abandoned. Most of these early associations were not in a strict sense parasitic. The worms merely availed themselves of the stability of the coral colonies to entrench themselves in places where food was plentiful. Amicably in youth the two settled down together, the coral engulfing the worm with the growth of its stony skeleton, but leaving an opening through which the worm might come and go; the worm in return not interfering with the coral in its particular pursuit of happiness.

Such a relationship, however, is an invitation to disaster, corals and worms being what they are. The coral might engulf the worm to the point of imprisonment and death by suffocation, and the worm might riddle the coral until it dies. There is evidence that both these abuses had occurred before the Devonian period was far under way. In the end the more active worms apparently got the better of the bargain because their descendants are still in the sea. Many of the corals, on the other hand, disappeared before the close of the period, victims presumably of old age but not of old age alone.

Perhaps the most striking example of ancient parasitism is the conjunction of the crinoids and those scavenging pigs of the sea, the capulid snails. The crinoids, popularly known as sea lilies, are not lilies. They are animals resembling starfishes which live rooted like plants to the floor of the sea. The capulid snails, whose name and appearance suggest the pointed cowl of a monk, possess no other observable qualification for monkhood. Partnerships between these two are abundantly memorialized by fossils from the Ordovician, Silurian, Devonian, and Carboniferous systems. In the beginning the snail merely nestled within the arms of the

crinoid and feasted on waste from its body. With time,
however, the snail fastened itself more effectively to the
anus of the crinoid—in some cases growing lustily enough
to cover the entire dome of the crinoid and to bow it to
the ground. No one may say how much inconvenience and
harm this capulid custom imposed upon the crinoids at large.
It is only known that crinoids lost their dominance in
the seas, and the snails must have been at least partly to
blame.

III

The ancient shelter and feeding associations preserved
in fossils have doubtless not been the only incubators of
parasitism. The habit might well have arisen in ways no
fossil could record. It might well have grown from associations that were originally antagonistic rather than coöperative, wherein beasts of prey abandoned war for thievery.
Or it might have developed in a variety of other ways—
and probably did.

A fly, for example, whose ancestors had laid their eggs
in the putrefying flesh of dead animals, might abandon
tradition and lay its eggs in a wound on a live one. Its
status would shift therewith from scavenger to parasite.
Similarly, many animals are born with a distaste for light,
and, like the mole, must find their place in the dark. If that
place happens to be the inside of a neighbor, parasitism
might result. Or a female in search of a sheltered spot to
lay her eggs might choose the flesh of another creature.
Under these diversities, however, one constant persists: the
urge to live as easily as possible.

And too, under the diversities in the results of parasitism,
certain general truths may be discerned. One parasite robs
its host of food, another of blood; some poison their hosts

and others castrate them. Some multiply so prodigiously that they tax their hosts into the grave, but not in most cases before they have mated and insured their own survival. For any parasite that eliminates its host too quickly also eliminates itself. No one may know to what extent society has been purged by the operations of parasites who were too eager on hosts who were too weak. One only knows that parasitism like predacity works toward equilibrium. Both like water tend generally to find their levels, where offense and defense are balanced.

Had not half of creation developed a resistance against the attacks of the other half, life would long since have returned to the muck. It is only when the equilibrium is disturbed that parasitism changes from a tolerable inconvenience to a terrible menace for the host. The antelopes, koodoos, and wildebeestes of Africa have long since learned to carry the trypanosomes of sleeping sickness in their blood with no observable discomfort. But let horses, oxen, or men—who lack any inherited immunity to the ravages of these microbes—become infected, and they quickly sicken and die.

Despite its boon of comfort and safety to the parasite, parasitism—from an evolutionary point of view—is more baneful to him than to his host. For all confirmed parasites, except the simplest one-celled plants and animals, are degenerate.

To discover the ultimate possibility in parasitic debasement one must study the crabs. These animals are fated to endure not only the trials which are the universal penalty for mortality, but also certain other afflictions designed for their special bedevilment. Many a crab develops in its abdomen a condition suggestive of a tumor, which arrests its growth and impairs its power of procreation. Dissection of the tumor reveals a mass of fibers that ramify like the

roots of a plant to every corner of the crab's anatomy, suck-
ing nourishment from the tissues as a plant sucks nourishment from the soil. In avoiding the nerves and the heart
the malignant thing displays such astuteness as men would
arrogate to themselves alone, for by thus sparing the life
of the crab it also prolongs its own.

Study has shown what no one could ever have guessed—
that the tumorous growth is no autochthon sprung from
the failing field of the crab's own flesh but a poacher from
another preserve. For when time is ripe a brood chamber
takes form in the tumor whence a multitude of active little
creatures emerges. Each one has three pairs of appendages,
a short food canal, one eye placed like that of Polyphemus
in the middle of the forehead, and a speck of a brain. After
swimming for a time the larva goes blind and assumes the
appearance of a water flea. It seeks out a crab and, burrowing through the armor to the arteries, becomes a blood-
thirsty Mr. Hyde with little resemblance to its former self.
Eventually it takes the form of a hernia-like sac on the belly
of the crab beneath the tail, nothing now but a mass of reproductive tissue and an appetite.

Thus *Sacculina* shows how far the angels may fall. If his
larval development means anything, he was once an active
and self-supporting crustacean; today he is an idler and a
thief. He is perhaps the most striking example of parasitic
decadence in the world. But there are many others who
are like him in kind if not in degree. They have exchanged
their organs of locomotion for organs of attachment; they
have subordinated all special senses to the primitive sense of
touch, and all special functions to the primitive functions
of eating and reproducing. In doing so they have sacrificed
all hope of progress for themselves and their descendants.
For it was Nature's plan to make easy the entrance to degeneracy but impossible the escape.

IV

No one viewing this spectacle of parasitism can fail to see the faces of men among the actors. The very name of parasite, with its implication of feeding through the flattery of a host, was invented to express a human situation. No one can fail to see that many of the methods whereby the dumb animals exploit their fellow animals are used by man against his fellow man. Men, to be sure, do not ordinarily consume the substance of one another, but they achieve essentially the same end through expedients of their own.

Parasitic exploitation like predatory war occurs normally between creatures of different species. Real creatures are not as clever as the apocryphal worm Ouroboros who feeds exclusively on himself. Because perpetual motion is no more practicable in the biological than in the physical world, any species that depended habitually and wholly on itself for nourishment would soon be relieved of the necessity to seek it.

Parasitism of man on man is possible partly because it does not affect all men and partly because it does not levy its tax directly on human flesh. It is social rather than organic. But that does not prevent its being a sly and greedy Shylock to the human race. Indeed, the interspecific parasitism of other creatures—like their interspecific predacity—is all too accurately and fully reproduced among men.

Some years ago Jean Massart, a biologist, and Emile Vandervelde, a sociologist, at the university of Brussels compared notes on the phenomena of parasitism. They found several examples of organic parasitism in plants and animals that were strikingly paralleled by examples of social parasitism in men. The book * they wrote on the subject

* *Parasitism Organic and Social* by Jean Massart and Emile Vandervelde, Swan Sonnenschein and Co., Ltd. London 1895.

has long since gone the way of most books, but the parallels remain.

The biologist observed that there are only three stores which plants and animals may draw upon for food: the air and earth of the mineral world on which the green plants subsist; the excretions, dead bodies, and other byproducts of the organic world on which the saprophytes and scavengers subsist; and the living tissues of organisms on which the herbivores, carnivores, and parasites subsist. The sociologist observed that men make their living in three remarkably analogous ways.

In the first place, there are men who take sustenance like green plants directly from the larger world outside themselves. As hunters, fishermen, miners, and farmers, they exploit the raw materials of wealth. Despite obvious differences between such men and plants in the method and scope of their activities, the men occupy the same position in human society that the plants occupy in society at large. Both are basic producers.

In the second place, there are men who live on the waste products of production and the residues of consumption. Beach-combers, rag-pickers, old-clothes men—to say nothing of the destitute in the slums of the world—manage on the crumbs that are brushed from the tables of the more fortunate. These are the scavengers of human society.

In the third place there are men who neither tap the fundamental reservoirs of wealth nor nose a living from the refuse of their neighbors. Like the herbivores and carnivores of the animal world they live instead on their neighbors, and on one another. And like the herbivores and carnivores in the society of organisms at large, they constitute the most varied and conspicuous element in the society of men.

They include the men whom our authors call predatory

exploiters, those who destroy their fellows outright to enrich themselves. A comfortably remote example of the type may be found in certain savage and barbarous communities which have waged wars of extermination on one another very much in the manner of termites and ants. Also in this group are the mutualists who engage in manufacture, transport, commerce, and government work. These men exchange an equivalent of service for the raw materials that sustain them, and the division of their labors is not unlike that of certain ants. Finally but, alas, not least in the group are the parasites who consume without producing. All other classes contribute to their ranks: farmers grown rich and lazy, beach-combers turned beggars and soldiers turned thieves, public servants that serve only themselves.

Whatever their origin the parasites in human society may be classified according to their methods of operation. They may be proprietary parasites living handsomely and without effort in the social body like tapeworms in the intestines of dogs, by controlling the machinery of production. These are the capitalists of the Marxian lingo, the economic royalists of a later terminology. Though some who have been given the hateful labels of this class are true parasites that feed on unearned riches, others have worked hard for the amenities they enjoy and are not parasites at all. Philosophers in their indigence and reformers in their ardor, however, sometimes fail to make this distinction.

Human parasites may also be political, like many of the courtiers of old and many of the remembered forgotten men of today. Whether he draws 18,000 livres a year as Steward of the Royal Hunt for signing his name twice a year, or a lesser sum for leaning on a shovel as ward of the W.P.A., the political parasite may always be recognized by one diagnostic trait. He always mimics however feebly some function that is useful to society at large.

Human parasites may specialize in the exploitation of sex. They may live by the prostitution of themselves, their children, or their wives. They may keep houses or they may exact toll from the keepers of houses. This class is less abject biologically than spiritually because it cannot exist without effort. The prostitute and the pimp must display their wares attractively, the brothel keeper must run her business efficiently. The most prosperous sexual parasites belong also to the proprietary and predatory classes, as Mr. Dewey has recently and dramatically revealed.

The predatory human parasites in the classification of Massart and Vandervelde are those that rob by fraud or force. Unlike the predatory exploiters, they do not destroy their hosts outright nor risk such a fate for themselves. They are the human equivalent of such animal pests as the gnat and the mosquito: the usurers, professional burglars, pickpockets, and others of their ilk. They are the least parasitic of all parasites, and have been known in more than one instance to rise to the status of bonafide predators. Bands of Arabs in the oases of North Africa and gangs of racketeers in the cities of North America have come in more than one instance merely to rob, but have remained to rule.

Proprietary, political, sexual, and predatory parasites are alike in that they generally appropriate part of the food supply of their hosts directly. Many other parasites work less directly. There are, for example, the satellites that swarm around men of power, winning advantages through friendship or kinship that they could never win through ability. There are others that make use of diplomas, oratory, or merely an impressive beard to disguise their incompetence and thereby to win emoluments they do not deserve.

So endlessly may the categories of human parasitism be illustrated. We may disagree with Massart and Vandervelde in their definition of the categories and in their selection of illustrations, but we may not deny that parasitism is rampant among men. Nature, indeed, has made men the most versatile parasites on earth.

Yet Nature has been kind to men as to none other of her children. She has vouchsafed in their case a unique exception to an iron-clad rule, a hope for deliverance denied all other creatures. For the parasitism of men, in being more individual and imitative than racial and hereditary, is curable. The offspring of a tapeworm may only become another tapeworm, but the child of a man who inherits a tapeworm's wealth and leisure need not necessarily lead a tapeworm's life. He may use the power of his mind and spirit to save his honor. Mankind at large might do the same. But it might do so only after a sufficient number of intelligent men have grown sufficiently disgusted with things as they just happen to be.

Chapter VI

THE WAY OF LOVE

BEING disgusted with Nature, especially in the form of human nature, is one of the most typical if not one of the most universal attributes of man. Man is the only creature that is capable of disliking the creation and disapproving of itself. Shaping the cruel and nasty devices of survival to moral ends, or pretending to do so when doing so is not convenient, are two of his most characteristic pursuits. Indeed, in his ardor to reform and recolor what is intrinsically not so good, he tends to overlook what is intrinsically not so bad.

The ways of Nature are not invariably opposed to the ethical idealism of humanity, even though the post-Darwinian spokesmen of science have rather generally neglected to say so. What they generally say was perhaps best said by Thomas Huxley in his famous Romanes lecture of 1893. "The practice of that which is ethically best," concluded Huxley, "involves a course of conduct which, in all respects, is opposed to that which leads to success in the cosmic struggle for existence. In place of ruthless self-assertion it demands self-restraint; in place of thrusting aside, or treading down, all competitors, it requires that the individual shall not merely respect, but shall help his fellows; its influence is directed not so much to the survival of the fittest, as to the fitting of as many as possible to survive. It repudiates the gladiatorial theory of existence."

Nature, however, as Darwin himself well knew, did not wait for man to repudiate the gladiatorial theory of existence. In view of eventuations, it is just as well that she didn't. Long before the coming of man she repudiated the theory herself, in some of her most cherished and most fundamental institutions. Though her end has always been the preservation of life regardless of the cost in lives, she has sought it to a considerable extent through coöperation as well as conflict.

She has sought it very largely through the great institution of nutrition. Eating and reproducing are the major functions of living, and both are phases of nutrition. Eating maintains the individual, reproduction the race. Only through reproduction could life in the aggregate have endured so long when in the individual it lingers so briefly. And only through a widespread coöperation of individuals could reproduction have achieved its objective. So it is that life is necessarily a self-contradictory procedure. Most individuals must maintain themselves by conflict and their species by coöperation.

Nature is a communist dictator who has never allowed an individual to amass any large or disproportionate percentage of its species' wealth. By placing strict limits on individual growth, she made certain in the beginning that the protoplasm available to any given species would be equitably divided among its members. To be sure, she has had certain favorites among species. She has kept all species of bacteria sufficiently small to be invisible to other creatures, while allowing certain whales ninety feet in length and an equivalent number of tons of weight. But she offset her gift of size to the whales by withholding the gift of vast numbers.

For the most part, however, Nature is dedicated to the concept that the safety of a species resides in a relatively large number of relatively small individuals. She has kept her children numerous by a simple device. She has arranged that they shall live chiefly through the surfaces of their bodies and organs, that with growth the surfaces shall increase less rapidly than the bulk. In other words, she has arranged that the more organisms or organs grow, the more difficult it shall become for them to grow further. She has arranged in this fashion that growth must ultimately stop at the size which she has ordained as standard for the species, and that where it stops reproduction shall begin.

So closely related are growth and reproduction that in some cases the two are virtually one. In many simple unicellular organisms, the latter process is merely a physiological continuation of the former. The organism eats until it reaches the limit which Nature has set on its growth, and then merely divides into two. In many simple multicellular organisms, growth and reproduction are almost as intimately related. The faster-growing parts of such organisms merely branch from their parents in buds, which ultimately set up housekeeping for themselves. Reproduction in both types is strictly a private affair.

Most creatures, however, have specialized organs for reproduction which are comparable to their organs for eating, breathing, and moving about. In some creatures these organs are extremely simple in their production of germ cells which are physiologically alike and equally capable of growing into new adults. In others the generative organs give rise to two physiologically different types of germ cells whose union produces the offspring. In certain species both male and female elements develop in the same individual. In most species they are separately housed in different individuals.

For those who seek evidence of conscious design in Nature, the prevalence of the sexual method of reproduction is a significant fact. For it is not only the commonest type of reproduction but on three counts at least it is also the most felicitous. It is the most economical because it affords the greatest number of offspring for the least amount of parental sacrifice. It is the safest because the germ cells are protected from the debilities which almost inevitably come to mature individuals, and accordingly are not apt to give rise to offspring with hereditary handicaps. It is the most creative because in its widespread bi-sexual phase it mixes the hereditary elements of the living jelly so as to prevent stagnation and encourage innovation.

Though an unqualified blessing to the race, bi-sexual reproduction is not invariably a blessing to the individual. In some cases it is painful and even deadly to the individual. There is the fly that must burst before she can lay her eggs, the salmon that spawns and then dies. There is the fierce rivalry for mates in so many species from crickets to men. The harshness that marks the process of nutrition carries over into reproduction.

It is with excellent reason that men speak of the sexual drive as a hunger. Eating and copulating are essentially similar phenomena throughout the animal world. Both are primarily devices of survival and both are intrinsically ruthless. Only through their power of self-delusion can men confuse the lust for copulation with the love that sometimes attends it.

Throughout the animal world, voracity marks the response to the sexual impulse. Sexual encounters are characteristically bloody. In many cases the hunger for food and the hunger for copulation rise to a peak together. There is the spider that first assimilates her consort's seed and then his entire person. There are the mice that kill and eat their wives, the wolves of both sexes that kill and eat one another. There are the biting and mauling that accompany the sexual act among primitive human beings. Though civilized people are inclined to replace the biting with kissing and to moralize on sublimation, they cannot escape the uncomfortable suspicion that their style of copulation is less ethically advanced than biologically degenerate.

Where in the face of these facts may one see any tendency to mutual aid in the function of impregnation, where any bonafide sentiment of tenderness or affection? Obviously one must look for these things beyond the function of impregnation, in other quite different phases of the reproductive process. One must look to the mothers that care for their offspring and to the fathers that sometimes help. One must look, in short, to the institution of the family. For it is by means of this institution that sexual reproduction leads its practitioners from conflict to co-operation. It is this institution, broadly conceived, that brings bees the strength of union in a hostile world; that brings young birds the protection of parental devotion when protection is desperately needed; that brings men such a solace as frequently abides after all other solace has departed.

II

There is a general feeling abroad today that family life is vanishing from the world of men; that when industrialism destroyed the home as a center for the production of goods, it all but destroyed the home as well. What once the members of a family did as a group under a single roof, they now do severally under many roofs. They work in the factory, the office, and the shop. They play in the dance hall, the motor car, and the cinema. They relax in the club and eat in the cafeteria. When they go home it is chiefly to sleep.

There is also a general feeling abroad that the moral as well as the physical bonds of family life are failing. Modern women have demanded freedom and to a large extent have

got it. Fathers and husbands no longer rule the roost because the rule as well as the roost is disappearing. They
can no longer dictate the lives of daughters and wives who
are economically independent, who are emotionally and
chemically able to have as few children and as many love
affairs as they desire.

From these and other ominous portents, such a thought-
ful writer as Langdon-Davies predicts the ultimate doom
of the old-fashioned home and family. He believes that
industrialism will destroy them utterly, no less in capitalistic than in communistic states; that, indeed, in Russia
and America it will do so first. One group of women will
become slaves in the factory as formerly they were slaves
in the home. Another will work in offices and shops,
economically and emotionally free from the compulsions
of a stable marriage. Another will become completely
parasitic, but with such perfect control over their male
hosts as to make them mere automatons. This group, according to Langdon-Davies, will rule the world, and their
idle whims will motivate it. The only domesticated women
of the old school will be a few dull peasants, raising their
children and their chickens in the country.

The moralists are hardly more flattering or reassuring.
They agree with Langdon-Davies that family life is sinking toward the grave, but (being for the most part women
who love their freedom) they do not see the emancipation
of women as the cause. They see, instead, the decline of
religion, and the rise of movies, automobiles, and drink.
Above all they see the ogre of sex.

Beneath this cynicism and alarm is the tacit assumption
that the family is a tender bloom which must surely wither
if women be allowed to work and to sin as men do; that
only in a hothouse of fear and oppression may it thrive.
There is a tacit assumption that the family is something

which society puts on as casually as a fop puts on a bouton-
nière, and as capriciously throws it away. There is, in
short, a feeling that the family is synonymous with the
marriage conventions which happen to house it in certain
civilized societies today; that the one must crumble with
the other.

The form of marriage, to be sure, has been as fragile as
glass. Man is the only animal that ever lacked automatic
and unquestionable answers to the problems of sex because
he is the only animal that ever possessed an imagination
and a conscience. Insofar as human history has had any
special significance in the dictionary of terrestrial biog-
raphy, it has dealt with the attempt to impose some sort
of moral order on the crude expedients of existence. Insofar as it has had any significance, it has also dealt with a
chronic dissatisfaction in the results.

From the beginning, men have sought the perfect compromise between their sexual instinct and their honor, and
from the beginning they have failed to find it. But though
the form of the compromise has varied vastly, certain
fundamentals of human nature have remained essentially
the same. When contemporary alarmists assume that the
collapse of the home and Victorian morality is necessarily
synonymous with the collapse of the human family, they
abandon history for hysteria. The ancestors of men lived
in families long before they lived in clothes. There are
good reasons for believing that the family is as inherent
in the nature of men as the quack in the nature of
ducks.

The complex mixture of animal associations on earth is a
broth that has been boiling for more than a billion years.
By putting together what the paleontologist, the biologist,
and the anthropologist know of these associations, something may be learned about when and how and why the

family relationship eventually stewed forth. That it did not result from an arbitrary flip on the part of some human cook is obvious from even a cursory glance at the evidence.

The one-celled organisms constitute the simplest form of life on earth today. They also suggest what may have been its earliest form, in a day so remote that not even fossils have survived to record it. Between these organisms and men lies the widest gap in the living world. An amoeba is not only simpler than a man. It is fundamentally different.

A man is an elaborate society within himself. He is a multitude of individuals called cells combined in a lesser multitude of counties called tissues, which in turn are gathered into states that are known as organs. Each has its individual and its corporate pursuits. Over all presides the dictatorship of the brain, with storm troops of nerves that reach into every corner of the kingdom.

An amoeba, on the other hand, is a completely autonomous unit, the only thorough-going individualist that ever lived. In one cell invisible to the eye, he performs many of the functions which a whale performs with a body of eighty tons. He eats without stomach or gut, breathes without gills or lungs, travels without fins, wings or legs, reproduces without organs of reproduction, and makes his way in the world without a nervous system to direct him.

He is as unsocial in his relationship with his fellows as he is undepartmentalized within himself. No one has ever described any tribal customs among the amoebae. Though a million of them may attack the unhappy colon of a white man in the tropics, there is no observable organization of their forces, no controlled division of the spoils. Each one is a rugged individualist.

The love life of the amoeba is equally rugged. Moralists who dislike him for his predatory propensities will dislike him even more for his amours. For these have little demonstrable connection with reproduction, and are casual to an extreme. When an amoeba gets enough food to grow large, he reproduces by the simple device of dividing in two. His occasional act of conjugation is not necessarily preliminary to the process, and indeed has been known to retard it.

When two amoebae clasp and exchange their internal liquors, the entire body of each seems to function as a sexual organ. When the encounter is over each one goes its private way, most likely never to meet the other again. No family relationship has ever been known to embrace it or to follow it. Biologists can not yet define the nature of the tonic inherent in this simplest of sexual acts. Its benefits, whatever they may be, are purely personal.

Nobody surely knows that the amoeba is a replica of the prototype creatures of the world. But it is surely known that in a general way two tendencies have marked the evolution of life in time. One was the tendency for creatures to grow progressively more complex. The other was the tendency for sex to become less the servant of the individual and more the slave of the race. The family relationship was the logical fruit of the union of these two tendencies.

The anatomical and social gulf between a one-celled amoeba and a many-celled sponge is wide. Nobody knows when, how, or even if it was bridged in a strict genetic sense. It is only known that sponges are preserved in the oldest fossiliferous strata on earth, and that they are the oldest tokens of organization in the animal world: the organization of mutually dependent cells in the bodies of living animals, and of mutually dependent animals in a colony. If these creatures were as similar to living sponges in physiology as they are in form and structure, they are also the oldest tokens of the conscription of sex to the purpose of reproduction.

Nature consumed an untold eon in bridging the gulf between the earliest sponges and the earliest insects. She consumed another eon in evolving the flowering plants, and with them such socially advanced insects as the bees. But the differences between a sponge and a bee are fully commensurate with the time that was taken to produce them.

During that time the elaboration of animal life had reached its first great climax. Anatomy had become in the bee a complex of special organs. Social union had become in the hive a complex of special duties. Sex had become an elaborate mechanism not only for reproduction but also for the variation of hereditary strains. For sponges are hermaphrodites that produce both male and female cells, and are consequently exposed to the dangers of inbreeding. Bees, on the other hand, are guarded against these dangers because male and female cells are housed in separate individuals.

With the physical improvements in the mechanism of sex came psychic improvements of even greater survival value. When a sponge reproduces, his services to his race are over. When bees reproduce, the offspring become a community responsibility. The worker bees are not the mothers of the grubs they so carefully tend, but the mothering instinct is in them—and with it the germ of the family relationship.

It is likewise present in all the animals whose ancestors presumably bridged the eon that separates the social insects and civilized men. It is present in the males no less (and sometimes even more) than in the females. It is present in the cold-blooded female salmon who knows no love of mate, but who scoops a trough in the bed of a stream for the harborage of her eggs. It is decidedly present in the little male stickleback who builds a nest in the water and guards the contents with his life. It is present in the male of the Chilian frog who carries his brood in a ventral pouch like a mother kangaroo. It is present in the female python who coils round her eggs like a brooding hen. In the warm-blooded birds and mammals, who know the love for offspring and in some cases the love for mate as well, the family relationship has grown from a germ to a fully fledged reality.

Selective courtship, agreeable partnership, and responsible parenthood are the essentials of this relationship in its highest form. They were the inevitable result of the evolutionary drive towards a safer propagation of life. They were a billion years in the making. It is no aspersion on man as a destroyer to presume that he cannot kill them in a day.

III

These qualities were destined to flower irregularly but richly in the mammals who lay crushed for long ages in a reptilian world. When finally freedom came with the dawn of the Cenozoic era, the mammals rose in triumph to rule the earth. Diverging to every far corner of the globe, they also diverged in habit and form. Some went down to the sea and became whales; some went up to the air and became bats. Some burrowed in the ground and became moles; some put on weight and became elephants. Many took to running over the grassy plains and became horses, antelopes, and sheep; others took to chasing them and became cats and dogs. A few made their home in the trees and became monkeys and apes. But wherever they went and whatever they became, they probably lived in family groups.

Endlessly diverse though mammals are in form and habit, there are only two fundamentally different types of family relationship among them. One type occurs in monkeys, apes, and men, who are perennial lovers. The other occurs in all other mammals, who are seasonal.

Responsible parenthood is the basic essential of family life, and both these types embrace it. But in the seasonal mammals the responsibilities of parenthood are grossly neglected by the males, and the other essentials are all but neglected by male and female alike. Marriage is neither carefully contracted nor faithfully preserved. So far as the mating pair is concerned, it exists only during and for the sexual act because the sexes are attracted to one another only when the females are in heat. At such times they mate with no fastidiousness of choice, with no loyalty to the companion of a previous season, and with no qualm over parting when the fever cools. At other times they may even be mutually antagonistic, sulking alone like the lion or banding together in hostile male and female herds like the buffalo and the seal.

It has frequently been observed that whereas the males among brooding birds are rather generally fine husbands and fathers, the males among seasonal mammals rather generally are not. Nature's expedients are invariably practical. A mother antelope, for example, is handicapped but not helpless. She can fight off enemies and gather food for herself and her offspring without any help from her mate. The result is that she seldom enjoys his help. The sitting robin, on the other hand, would starve or be murdered without the coöperation of her mate. Because robins would soon disappear without this coöperation, Nature sees that the sitting robin invariably gets it.

For those who consider the presence of a helpful father essential to a worthwhile family, the seasonal mammals are indeed a disappointment when compared with the brooding birds. They may even appear to embody a reversal of evolution. Nature's purpose, however, is never sentimental. She contrived the family as a device to keep the species alive through parental care of the young. If one parent can adequately supply this protection alone, the requirements for a family from her point of view are met.

Many of the males among the perennially erotic mammals are no nearer perfection as husbands and fathers than are the males of the seasonal mammals. Yet in the family relationships of the perennially erotic we can see at least the promise of that perfection. Moralists who call the perennial eroticism of men beastly choose a strange adjective to express their disapprobation. Perennial eroticism is peculiarly an attribute of man and his manlike kin. Not only that, but it is the attribute which more than any other has made possible the fullest flowering of the family relationship. For only among mates with a year round sexual need for one another could the year round partnership of the human family develop.

Moralists who emphasize the differences between apes and men do so perhaps because they are shocked by the similarities. The differences between the two are so few and slight that biologists do not hesitate to place them both in the same sub-order of the animal kingdom. The similarities are so many and great that paleontologists and anthropologists do not hesitate to ascribe to both a common origin, and to see in the present condition of the one a convincing reflection of a previous condition of the other.

Baboons are not the most manlike of the subhuman anthropoids, but they are the most manlike that thrive in captivity. Large colonies of them have been long maintained and deeply studied. Attempt has been made to duplicate in these colonies the conditions of the natural environment. Inasmuch as baboons are not notably self-conscious, their behavior there is probably not far from normal.

What especially distinguishes it from the behavior of seasonal mammals is not only the incessant preoccupation with sex, but the lengthy associations which in some cases grow out of it. Measured by the standard of Christian ethics these associations are not ideal. They are polygamous whenever there are enough females to make polygamy possible, and whenever there are males sufficiently strong to commandeer more females than their share. Though adultery has seldom been observed in a baboon colony, it is outlawed by the jealousy and possessiveness of the male rather than by the love and devotion of the female. Though children are carefully nursed by their mothers, they are overlooked by their fathers; and as soon as they can walk they are spurned by both. ·Yet under the crudity of the baboon harem are the rudiments of the family in its human form: the union of husband, wife, and child.

Propinquity is not the only ingredient of love between a man and a woman today, but it is the fundamental one. Similarly, it must have been fundamental in the racial development of that emotion. Love as practised by baboons today may yesterday have been practised by the ancestors of men. And just as perennial sexual hunger made possible this primitive type of love by lengthening the association of mates, so also it made possible the more idealized types.

The manlike apes are biologically as far above the baboons in manlike qualities as man is above the manlike apes. The brutal dominance of the male baboon gives way in the chimpanzee to gentler tactics. Indeed, though the elaborate courtship of this ape does not include any honeyed words or maudlin verse, it is similar in most other details

to human courtship. The marriage that follows is not
performed at an altar, but it is based on mutual consent
without coercion. The love that initiates the marriage is
not Platonic, imperishable, or exclusive, but it fosters com-
panionship at least for a while between compatable mates
and their offspring. As such it may well epitomize an early
stage in the ennoblement of human passion.

No one precisely knows what manner of love may lie
between the manlike apes and man. The ancestors of men
were probably a large-brained model of the chimpanzee,
and their family relationship was doubtless commensur-
ably advanced. They probably roamed through the forests
in little polygamous family groups, because food in the
forest is generally too scarce and scattered to sustain any
larger or more stationary organization. But the germs of
cunning and invention were in their heads. They varied
their diet of fruit with meat, and later with food which
they raised for themselves. The aisle that led from the
forest to the farm was a long and dangerous passage. From
fighting its dangers humanity was born. From fighting its
dangers in family groups, the human type of altruistic love
was probably also born.

IV

Unfortunately, no one knows how the human family
was organized when it emerged from the woods. No one
knows how it first came to be built into the structure of
tribal society, nor what forms it assumed in the process.
Indeed, there is no problem in the entire domain of science
more complicated by a dearth of facts and a plethora of
prejudiced debate.

Inasmuch as nothing is definitely known about the social life of early man, his habits may only be inferred from

the habits of such primitive men and apes as exist today. What inferences are drawn depend pretty generally on the motives of those who do the drawing. The habits of living apes and primitive men are highly diverse. They may be used—and frequently have been used—to prove practically anything about early man.

When the Darwinian theory fell upon the citadels of Victorian smugness in the middle of the nineteenth century, a great need was felt to do something about it. The first impulse was to destroy it with the potent virus of ecclesiastical disputation, but this proved not potent enough. The next impulse was to warp it to the service of established beliefs and institutions, and in this the established powers were highly successful. They convinced a great number of intelligent people that things as they were had become so through the process of natural selection, that they represented the survival of the fittest in the flux of human society. All that the ruling classes of the day believed in was thus shown to be approved by Nature herself.

Robert Briffault, V. F. Calverton, and many other contemporary scholars have demonstrated in detail how ably the science of anthropology rose to this occasion. They have shown how Edward Westermarck in particular presented the authorized monogamous Victorian family as the final link in an evolutionary chain, the ultimate victory of a drive toward monogamy which even the simian ancestors of men had felt. They have shown how Westermarck's writing embraced a mass of selected "evidence" in support of this assumption. Not only were primitive living men and apes presumed by Westermarck to possess an instinct for monogamy, but cats, whales, and the not otherwise moral wolves. Even the indifferent hippopotamus was pictured as an affectionate and faithful lover. The absurdity of Westermarck's allegations in the face of known facts was no more remarkable than the innocence with which they were embraced by the vast majority of Victorians.

To be sure, there were some who demurred. Radical thinkers attempted to show that monogamy was not the product of instinct but of economics, a response to environmental and not to internal forces. Though Engels, Kautsky, Plechanov, and other Marxian philosophers made a good case for the thesis that monogamy is the product of poverty rather than idealism, it was part of the idealism of most of their contemporaries not to listen.

Today the battle lines are better balanced. A more dispassionate science in a less self-satisfied society is laying the myth of the monogamous instinct. Though such able researchers as H. S. Jennings and B. Malinowski continue to support it, they represent a cause that is steadily losing ground among scholars and laymen alike.

As anthropological investigations progress, it becomes increasingly reasonable to conclude that the human family underwent no uniform development the world around, and no consistent development in any specific tribe or race. Man is an opportunist who shifts his habits with a shifting environment. Under different conditions in different parts of the world today, polygamy, polyandry, and monogamy are all workable and consequently respectable forms of the family relationship. They were probably so from the beginning.

Anthropologists have loaded our libraries with descriptions of marriage customs and taboos, the variety of which is an overwhelming proof that no one form of the family may alone be considered "natural" in man. What is "natural" is that there be some emotional union of mother and child, which in some cases includes the father.

Demonstrating that the monogamous family is probably not the product of a progressive development does not destroy the likelihood that the maternal instinct is. It does not destroy the fact that this instinct is the basis of family life in man as in other creatures. There is evidence to show that tenderness between mates is rooted in the mother instinct, and strongly to suggest that the roots may have grown in an evolutionary manner through time.

The young of living mammals are not all equally dependent on their parents. A calf is on its feet at birth and off milk a few weeks or at most a few months later. The young of the undomesticated grazers are comparably self-reliant. In the herbivorous mammals generally, the maternal instinct is brought into play during a relatively small percentage of their lives. Their family organization is accordingly loose, and the amenities born of family life are on a relatively primitive level.

Differentiated on the basis of the length of time the young are helpless and dependent, there are several types of mammals between cattle and the men who keep them. Each type may be placed on its appropriate level in a stairway that leads from cattle to men. Cats, for example, may be placed a little higher than cattle because kittens are helpless for a somewhat longer time than calves. Monkeys, by the same token, may be placed considerably higher than cats, apes higher than monkeys, and man on top. The successive levels on which these types are located correspond in general to the successive levels of geologic time at which they first appeared. It would seem from this that the mammals evolved through species whose young were progressively more dependent on parental care, and that the family relationship evolved with them. In man whose young are the most helpless on earth, the family reached a climax of development.

No one knows precisely through what channels the maternal instinct evolved. It is a safe assumption, however, that they were more complicated than this speculation implies. Nature does not share man's passion for generalization. She prefers rather to hide significance in irrelevance, order in irregularity. But despite the irrelevancies and irregularities which confuse the evolution of the maternal instinct, its significance and its direction are reasonably clear.

It is reasonably clear that the maternal instinct is the nucleus of family life, and that it gave rise with time to tighter and longer associations of mother and offspring. It is reasonably clear that the affection thus engendered reached out to embrace the male. It is less clear how the father came to reciprocate as well as to receive the mother's affection. The year round sexual relationship among the perennially erotic anthropoids provides the propinquity which is essential to altruistic love. But so far as it is merely sexual it does not provide the motive.

Robert Briffault in "The Mothers" presents a masterful discussion of the manner whereby the male may possibly have come to feel the tender and abiding sentiments of love. He argues that these sentiments are in direct opposition to the brutal and periodic sexual impulses of the male, that the former could not conceivably have evolved from the latter. He argues that they probably evolved directly from the maternal instinct, through the genetic and sociological channels that connect young males and their mothers.

Certainly in species whose young are helpless for a long period of time, there is an excellent reason why the services of the male should not stop with impregnation. Any masculine coöperation in the discharge of maternal duties is an added safeguard to such species. Safeguarding species is

Nature's first concern, and that is undoubtedly why she insisted on at least a modicum of masculine coöperation among the higher anthropoids, whatever may have been her means of bringing it about.

Love as opposed to lust in the human species was, according to Briffault, at first confined pretty largely to the women. The capacity for sympathy, compassion, affection, benevolence, and generosity spread with time from the women to their offspring and mates. Briffault believes that these sentiments are not yet wholly instinctive in the male, that he acquires what he can boast of them very largely through education.

Some males may reject these ideas on the evolution of the paternal virtues, but no one may reasonably doubt that the family is rooted deeply in time. Its essential ingredient, the union of mother and child, is as venerable as hair and skin. Those who fear that it is rapidly crumbling today are thinking less of the family than of its monogamous form.

No one may deny that monogamy has many enemies, some of ancient lineage and some that are very modern. One of the quaint inconsistencies of the twentieth century is the decrease of individual freedom in the state and its simultaneous increase in the bedroom. Though grandmother's voice still calls from the grave, it is no longer the universal law on love because it no longer universally fills the young with fear. Many may deplore it and a few may attempt to change it, but no one may deny that sex for the sake of sex alone is in the midst of a renaissance.

The current trend is only in keeping with the precedent of human history. Civilized man's adjustment to his sexual impulse has always been as violent and irrational as the impulse itself. Periods of license have mothered chiefly unthinking disgust and fear; periods of repression, unthinking lust and revolt. No other animal has ever been so violently at odds with itself. For no other animal has ever had the conscience to be at times so moral, nor the imagination to be at other times so immoral.

The present period of sexual freedom, however, differs from all its predecessors. In these differences lies the promise of a future compromise between the physical and moral natures of man happier than he has generally achieved in the past. Contraceptives are fairly reliable antidotes for the more virulent physical and emotional poisons of sex. They have already made sex less dangerous than it ever has been before. No doubt they have made promiscuous intercourse easier than it ever has been before. But by restricting the family to a size that is desirable to the parents and advantageous to the children, contraceptives have also made it more difficult for the sensual to destroy the spiritual values of human affection.

Sex, to be sure, is still a difficult and dangerous business. It is still very considerably an undirected individual adventure followed very often by an unsuspected individual disaster. But the youths of the modern world know increasingly more than their parents knew. Though they are in a position to sin without paying all the traditional wages of sin, they are also in a position to see that the Freudian horrors of repression are only one phase of the danger of sex. They are in a position to see that opposition to the reckless play of the sexual instinct was never mothered entirely by the envious impotence of the old, nor fed wholly on the fear of bastardy and disease. With their unprecedented knowledge of sexual physiology and psychology, they are in a position not only to avoid the disasters of unrestrained indulgence but also to discover the pleasures of reasoned control.

The moralist is inclined to forget that the sexual freedom of the modern world is not exclusively the freedom of debauch. It is also the freedom to enjoy and promote the durable satisfactions of love. Sexual conquest is still one of the supreme acts of self-assertion among men. It probably always will be. But unless the trend of a billion years turns back upon itself, sex will never exist widely for itself alone. Men will never universally adopt the habits of the amoeba.

Indeed, unless the trend of a billion years reverses, sex should become increasingly subservient to the family—to the family not only as a reproductive, but also as a social unit. The family should grow more rather than less tightly knit. Monogamy might well become its real as well as its authorized form among a gaining percentage of civilized men and women.

Chapter VII

THE BROADER BROTHERHOODS OF FLESH

Historical facts grow lush on an earth whose years are numbered by indefinite millions and whose inhabitants have been too numerous to be numbered at all. Prejudices grow lush in a species whose habits include the appraisal of facts more by whim than by reasoned judgment. Vigorously claiming to reveal the laws that determine the facts of Nature—and as vigorously disputing each other's claim— the convictions of men may reveal little more than a state of mind or merely a state of digestion.

So it is that even while pessimists are making long faces because of the conflict in the living world, optimists are expanding in smiles because of its coöperation. Even while Thomas Huxley was claiming the first decisive victory for the former, others were confidently claiming the same for the latter. "We may safely say," wrote Kropotkin in his famous essay on "Mutual Aid Among Animals," "that mutual aid is as much a law of animal life as mutual struggle." Quoting what he conceived to be Nature's advice to her offspring, he ended the essay with these words: " 'Don't compete!—competition is always injurious to the species, and you have plenty of resources to avoid it. . . . Therefore combine—practise mutual aid! That is the surest means for giving to each and to all the greatest safety, the best guarantee of existence and progress, bodily, intellectual and moral.' . . ."

We have the assurance of Henry Drummond that Nature's offspring rather generally took the advice. Drummond, who was stronger than Kropotkin in his control of the exclamation point, was weaker in his control of the capital letter. In "The Ascent of Man" he grudgingly conceded that "the first chapter or two of the story of evolution may be headed the Struggle for Life." "But take the book as a whole," he continued, "and it is not a tale of battle. It is a Love-story." When Drummond wrote "Love" as he frequently did in the course of his lengthy argument, he meant "Love" to the fullest capacity of the capitalization.

Even Gilbert White, who was second to no one in shrewd appraisal of values in the living world, had his own emotional moments. The world must have seemed all harmony and peace when he wrote of the Hampshire cattle standing in ponds, their dung dropping in the water to become food for aquatic insects which in turn became food for fishes. "Thus Nature, who is a great economist," White drolly concluded, "converts the recreation of one animal to the support of another." In a more characteristic mood he would doubtless have noticed that all was not harmless play and barter in this tender scene. The insects that went down the gullets of the fishes, had they been philosophical and not too hurried, would doubtless have persuaded him to qualify his conclusion.

The concept of coöperation among living creatures is as old as human thought and the foundation of many religions, but much of the "evidence" that supports it can hardly be called scientific. It is cherished more by the hungry emotions than by the ascetic mind. The men who have been best informed about plants and animals have been more impressed by their competitive than by their coöperative activities. Natural history, in fact, matured into science with a generalization of struggle as the basis of life and its evolution.

Darwin, to be sure, enlarged the Malthusian concept

of social competition in a crowded world to include all types of adversity that might possibly harass a living creature. A large part of his evidence, however, bore on the narrower concept. A large proportion of his followers has been content with the narrower concept. As Kropotkin put it, "they came to conceive the animal world as a world of perpetual struggle among half-starved individuals, thirsting for one another's blood. They made modern literature resound with the war-cry of *woe to the vanquished*, as if it were the last word of modern biology." Huxley, the ablest spokesman of all, was also one of the narrowest in this regard.

Though conflict is obviously not quite so prominent in the animal world as the Huxleys believe it to be, coöperation is obviously not quite so prominent as the Rousseaus believe it to be. Somewhere between Huxley's world of bloody strife and Rousseau's world of loving peace the real world stands.. Social relationships in that world reach from conflict to coöperation, even as human opinions about them reach from the pessimism of Huxley to the optimism of Rousseau. An impersonally just appraisal of these relationships is probably impossible. Those who seek the meaning of things may only hope that in being aware of the prejudices they carry on their backs they may somehow find ways of lightening the load.

Only an optimist's prejudice would deny that conflict is a fundamental part of Nature's plan for her children. The unavoidable necessity of eating creates the unavoidable necessity of being eaten. Only a pessimist's prejudice would deny that coöperation is also a fundamental part of Nature's plan. Family union, as we have seen, is a widespread and easily apparent attribute of life, in many cases as essential to racial survival as eating is essential to the survival of the individual. Furthermore, there is good evidence to show that larger and simpler coöperative associations exist beneath the family relationship. There is evidence to show that larger and more complex coöperative associations exist beyond it.

II

The most obviously significant cleavage in the living world is that which separates the animals from the plants. This cleavage, however, grows less obvious when we turn from the more to the less elaborate organisms. It all but disappears when we turn to the least elaborate. In many unicellular creatures the fundamental characters of plant and animal are blended. Some of these creatures may be met as plants in textbooks of botany and as animals in textbooks of zoölogy.

There is a cleaner cut cleavage in the living world than that which separates the animals from the plants: the cleavage between the unicellular and the multicellular organisms. It is only because of their minuteness as individuals that the vast and varied hordes of the former have not been given parity in the textbooks with the more conspicuous hordes of the latter. One might argue from good biological data that to classify organisms as single and many-celled, rather than as plants and animals, would be to recognize a more fundamental distinction.

From the pinnacle of human self-esteem, a creature that performs every function of life with a single cell is almost too crude for contempt. That such a creature may succeed in meeting its problems quite as effectively as more elaborate creatures meet theirs, is a fact not generally admitted or even observed. Yet the one-celled organisms have succeeded so well that they outnumber all other living things.

By reproducing through simple division they approach immortality more closely than do any others, because parents pass largely into their children and death is rather the result of accident than the inevitable end of each individual's life. Furthermore, the one-celled organisms are marvelously adaptable to food which no other creatures can stomach and to places no others can endure. They have conquered every environment from ocean deep to mountain crest, from the scalding waters of thermal springs to the frozen tundras of the North, from the dust in the air to the muscles and blood of their neighbors.

Their chief importance with reference to our present concern, however, does not lie in any of these things. It lies in the fact that the one-celled organisms are practically devoid of coöperative relationships. Apart from occasional conjugation, which bestows some obscure sort of mutual benefaction upon its practitioners, they live lives of intensely competitive individualism.

If the unicellular organisms of the modern world resemble the earliest inhabitants of the primordial world, as many scientists believe, their independence is a significant fact in evolution. For it then must follow that coöperation was absent from the earliest society on earth. No one, of course, can prove that this was so because the primordial world was too feverish in enacting its history to be careful in recording it. But certain records have survived to the present which throw some light on dark events.

Most one-celled organisms have emerged unpedigreed from the past. Unicellular plantlike creatures may truly have been the earth's first inhabitants, but they left no tangible records to prove it. The slime-molds, for example, have left no trace of themselves in the rocks of any age. The bacteria, which possibly were involved in the business of disease and decay since life began, have done only slightly better. Many shells and bones of fossil animals show lesions suggestive of infection; many woody plants of the coal beds show partial decomposition. Though this was probably the work of bacteria, no actual fossil imprint of a bacterium has ever been conclusively identified. Several alleged relics of this sort have been reported, but science is dubious about the preservation of soft-bodied creatures that measured ten thousand to the inch.

The one-celled diatoms are the simplest creatures with skeletons in the world today. Enclosed in beautiful boxes of silica, one two-hundredth of an inch across, they thrive in water both salt and fresh, as well as in soggy soil. In their dainty little yachts of glass the diatoms throng by the billions at the surface of the sea, or sink like Lilliputian submarines to greater depths. Those that escape the stomachs of their foes sink finally in death to the ocean floor. There their sturdy little skeletons defy decay and accumulate to an all but unbelievable extent. In the frigid abyss beneath Antarctic waters they clothe ten million square miles.

If life evolved in time through simple to complex organisms, we should expect such creatures as diatoms to provide the earliest fossil record of life on earth. Yet despite their primitiveness, toughness, and abundance today, diatoms are not known to be of extremely ancient lineage. They are first found in the relatively recent rocks of the Mesozoic era. In these and later formations their abundance and variety suggest a long and unshelled ancestry before that time, but what that ancestry may have been no one may surely say. The same is true of all other one-celled organisms. They may have owned the earth in the beginning of geologic history, but their deed of ownership is lost.

Though these facts are negative so far as the history of society is concerned, they are not without some significance. In failing to prove that the one-celled organisms were the earliest citizens of the world, they likewise fail

to prove that the extreme competitive individualism of
one-celled organisms was the earliest type of social relationship. One-celled existence in all its phases might for
all we know be merely a latter-day degeneration. There
is positive evidence to show, on the other hand, that co-
operation is an ancient principle in Nature, possibly more
ancient than the principle of competition.

The most abundant fossils in the primordial Pre-Cambrian
formations of the earth are the remains of certain primitive plants which botanists call blue-green algae. By some
strange perversity in the powers that order terrestrial affairs, these modest members of the living world are allowed
distinction in the physical world. Proliferating in chains
and sheets of cells which disturb the chemical balance of
the water that sustains them, they have repeatedly built
vast monuments to themselves. They help erect the ter-
raced temples at the mouths of modern hot springs. They
mold the minerals of sea water to little balls resembling the
eggs of fishes, which the waves may spread like a blanket
on the bottom or the winds heap high in dunes along the
shore. "Water biscuits," built of limestone plates to the
pattern of an onion through the agency of these plants, occur in rocks of every age.

So far as the record goes, the lime-secreting algae would
seem to have been the first decidedly successful organisms on earth. Deposits alleged to have been produced by
them have been reported by scientists from Pre-Cambrian
formations the world around. Together with certain less
abundant remains of sponges and worms, they constitute
the only organic relics of that distant day with any serious
claim to authenticity.

As the oldest reminders of life on earth these relics are
of peculiar interest. As the oldest testimonials to the cooperative union of cells they are of peculiar significance.

For they show that coöperation was a fundamental principle of life at the very beginning of its recorded history. The collaboration of cells toward a common objective is so widespread a phenomenon today that we overlook its significance. It is normally so smooth—in our own bodies, for example—that we accept it with indifference. We cannot, alas, accept with indifference the loss of that collaboration when our cells become competitive with cancer. And just as cancer is a mysterious curse, its reverse is a mysterious blessing.

Intercellular coöperation has been the basis of all observable progress in the living world. So far as we know, the mutually antagonistic one-celled organisms are not essentially different now from what they were at the beginning of their recorded history. They are numerous and successful, but they are also static. The many-celled organisms, on the other hand, have expanded from the algae of the Pre-Cambrian seas to the men of today, and the possibilities of living have expanded with them.

III

Most evolutionists believe that the expansion of living creatures in time has gone on in the continuous and logical fashion of a growing tree. The coöperative relationships of living creatures would seem to have developed in quite another fashion. They would seem to have developed at distinctly different levels which are comparable to the decks of a ship, and to have embraced a host of not very closely related species at each level.

They may merely appear to have done so, to be sure, because our knowledge of life is incomplete. Were our knowledge perfect, coöperative relationships might be seen to have grown to the well-known pattern of the single genealogical tree. On the other hand, there is just a possibility that they might have evolved—at least in part—without reference to the known devices of inheritance, through inherently different and discontinuous tendencies toward coöperation. There are many biologists to deny this possibility but there is none as yet to disprove it.

Sociologists, whose eyes are riveted on man, seldom look beneath man's simian relatives for the roots of coöperative living. Most biologists seldom look beneath the social insects. Yet at a biologic level far beneath the levels of ape and bee, coöperative living goes on widely in the world today. The student of fossils knows that it went on widely at this lower level long before bees and apes were born.

The distinguishing feature of coöperation at this level is that it consists exclusively in the physical conjunction of mutually dependent units. The Pre-Cambrian algae were the simplest creatures ever known to have formed associations of this type, but they were yet not so simple as they might have been. They had arrived at more of coöperation than the mere union of cells in the bodies of individuals: the union of individuals in colonies. But how they had arrived there and who their ancestors may have been are secrets which the rocks have not revealed.

Judging by the fossil remains of these colonies, they were the communist's dream of perfection come true. The microscopic plants that left impressive records of themselves as communities left no record at all of themselves as individuals. So intimate was their union that no one can precisely say from the fossils where the individual stopped and the state began. Poor preservation undoubtedly accounts for some loss of detail in the remains of ancient algal colonies, but even in modern colonies of the same type the individual is obscured by the group.

Furthermore, the colonies themselves lost much of their

individual identity by merging in reefs. Globular colonies a few inches to a foot across in reefs as great as ten feet long and four feet deep are common in Pre-Cambrian formations throughout the world. Not least among the marvels of Glacier National Park are the enduring monuments of this sort which the earliest known plants have erected to the earliest known federations of living creatures.

When later in Cambrian time fossils were first preserved in varied abundance, the lime-secreting algae continued their reef-building activities on a smaller scale. But with the dawn of the Cambrian period interest shifts from the algae because other quite different organisms appeared to play the dominant reef-building rôle. No one knows how these organisms originated. No one even knows exactly what they were, though they were probably animals related to the sponges or the corals.

The well-defined cups which these creatures secreted have double walls with radiating partitions between them. Nobody knows whether the creatures lived like sponges in the spaces between the walls or like corals in the central cavity. Nobody knows whether one or many individuals inhabited each cup. We do know, however, that the cups were jumbled and heaped by the millions in mighty reefs. By a strange coincidence the largest of these ancient reefs, 200 feet thick and 400 miles long, is preserved in Australia not far from the largest of modern coral reefs.

By a stranger coincidence the creatures that formed it were dead before the middle of the Cambrian period, as also were all their relatives elsewhere in the world. They constitute a nameless dynasty that came into the world without any known ancestor and left it without any known descendant. Yet, by developing strong communal associations which did not completely submerge the individuals that composed them, these mysterious creatures advanced the banner of coöperative living a little farther along its way. Indeed, by doing so they accomplished without trying what men can only hope to accomplish after trying very hard.

With the later periods of geologic time a great variety of sponges, bryozoans, corals, and coral-like animals advanced the banner still farther. Unfortunately, it is not possible to learn from the stony remains of these ancient colonial structures the precise relationships of the animals that built them. It would seem, however, that colonial integration and individual differentiation developed together, and that with time the development was in general towards greater and greater complexity.

Turning to the modern world, we can match every stage in the probable progression of the physically united colony. We can add stages which, because of the delicacy of the communities, were not even crudely recorded in the rocks. Many animals that feed on the one-celled organisms of modern oceans are blessed with far more than the average allotment of food. Certain whales belong to this privileged class, and it was Nature's whim to let them become the largest animals that ever lived. It was her whim to keep most others in the same class small. Many overfed pygmies proliferate in the shoal waters of the sea with the prodigality of jungle plants. They use their superfluous food to multiply by budding and branching, until innumerable individuals combine in such colonies as we have described above.

Thomson and Geddes have pointed out some interesting gradations in the intimacy and complexity of these associations. Sponge colonies, which occur in many places today, are formed by the fusion of budded individuals into large irregular masses. There is no trace of nervous connection between individual sponges, no suggestion of any division of labor in the colony. A shark might bite off a large chunk of such an aggregation without affecting anything but its size.

In the great hemispheres of the brain-corals of modern reefs, a somewhat closer integration of vital activities may be seen. Adjacent polyps may share a common stomach in the manner of Siamese twins, and nervous impulses may be transmitted from one part of the colony to another. Organ-pipe corals represent a further stage of integration, in that adjacent individuals are invariably connected by well-defined canals.

The beautiful "sea pens" of modern oceans have definite divisions of labor among the individuals that compose them. Certain polyps maintain a continuous stream of food-laden water through the colony, certain others seize the food as it passes by. Still others perform the tactile, reproductive, and defensive functions of the colony. The Portuguese man-of-war, a community of this type, represents the highest stage of complexity in the physically united colony. Embracing myriad individual polyps, it can yet contract, expand, sway, and swim as a unit. It can capture a fish in the manner of a single organism and then eat it in the manner of many.

The Portuguese man-of-war, to be sure, is not known to have descended from the sponges by way of certain specialized corals. It is merely the terminus of a functionally progressive series of modern colonial creatures, arbitrarily selected. Nobody knows precisely through what channels Nature moved from the simplicity of the Pre-Cambrian algae to the complexity of the contemporary Portuguese man-of-war. It is only known that she did so move, and that as a result a great many creatures were brought into obviously felicitous unions.

IV

As an effective corporation for the business of living, the physically united colony at its best can hardly be excelled. As an example of "Love" in Nature it is hardly more inspiring than the marriage of the large and the small intestine in man. Indeed, the organisms whose union makes such a colony as the Portuguese man-of-war are on a biological level with the organs whose union makes a man.

One need not be sentimental to see certain elements in the coöperative activities of men that are lacking in the cooperative activities of the organs of which men are composed. One need not be uncritically anthropomorphic to see that the federations of ants and men possess certain common attributes that distinguish them from the federations of algae and corals. Ants and men do not invariably or equally radiate intelligence and love, but they are held together in their respective unions by bonds which in a general sense are psychical and emotional rather than merely physical.

The evolution of psychically united societies is even more conjectural than the evolution of physically united colonies. Fossil shells and bones no longer fraternize or fight. They neither affirm nor deny our speculations about their private lives. Yet by fitting together what the paleontologist, the biologist, and the anthropologist know, certain reasonable guesses may be made.

The animals that band together in societies today are generally more complex than their colonial brethren. They are generally assumed to represent more advanced stages in evolution. However this may be, it is still true that colonies and societies are different rather in kind than in degree. To presume that the one grew out of the other in a genetic sense would be presumptuous indeed. They belong in different categories of natural phenomena, and any attempt to relate them must be made without benefit of scientific data.

Thomson and Geddes define the fundamental nature of a society. "A thousand passengers on a liner make an isolated aggregate of individuals, but they do not constitute a society. Yet if they were wrecked on an uninhabited oceanic island . . . they would begin to show corporate action. They would begin to act as a unity, as a whole which is more than the sum of its parts. Similarly with animals, there is nothing social in the multitudes of mites in the cavern of a cheese, but even a small community of ants is a societal form. Hard and fast lines are impossible; aggregate shades into integrate; but there is no mistaking even a feeble social note which is sounded whenever a group of individuals begins to act as a whole, with some self-subordination among the members."

Even a superficial look at the living world will reveal that full-fledged societies by this definition are relatively rare. Many aggregations of organisms are not societies; some are not even friendly. Fiddler crabs, for example, must flock together for some reason other than mutual entertainment because they fight as much as they fiddle. Herring gulls in their rookeries are as crowded as sardines in cans, but they are less complacent about being so. They viciously guard their private claims in the nesting area, and many are killed in the process. It is obvious that some special geographic advantage, or possibly some homing instinct, must bring such creatures together.

The world is full of gregarious animals whose gregariousness is not demonstrably the result of brotherly love. On the other hand, there are many examples of loose mutual toleration among animals that go in bands for the sake of some common advantage. Though in many cases the toleration does not rise to the level of true coöperation nor the bands to the status of true societies, such associations may sound "a feeble social note."

A great many gregarious unions which are not in a strict sense societies are yet socially beneficial to their members. Such are the herds of elk and deer, the communities of prairie dogs and beavers. These creatures get more than their just share of romantic adulation for their social virtues, and much that is written about their lives is crudely false. Gregarious mammals by and large are the least truly sociable, maternal, and intelligent of the so-called higher animals. Their glorification by the sentimentalists is a quaint if not a surprising phenomenon.

This, however, may be truly said for them. Though widely addicted to sexual and nutritional jealousies and to social and parental indifference, they gain advantages as groups which as individuals they lack. A herd is quicker than an isolated individual to sense the approach of an enemy because the most alert members are apt to be first to acquire the information, and to warn their duller comrades with their cries. Though the cries are raised through personal fear they result in social service. Similarly, a herd is better able than an individual to intimidate an enemy even though the constituents are interested exclusively in their own respective skins.

The enemy, on the other hand, is apt to work alone, although some predacious species are semi-gregarious. Lions and wolves are essentially solitary beasts, but they frequently hunt in family groups. Vultures are never alone in their feasting. When one of them drops from the sky on sighting a meal, others are sure to follow. There is no more concerted action among such predators and scavengers, however, than there is among their prey; no more subordination of individual to social objectives. There is merely a common desire for food among creatures that happen to be neighbors. Any good that may come from seeking it in groups is purely inadvertent.

Though most gregarious and semi-gregarious animals are opportunists in most of their relations with one another, it would be an oversimplification of the facts to conclude that all of them are always incapable of genuine social behavior. With the possible exception of the beavers, they are devoid of a strong social instinct, yet they frequently exhibit a tendency toward coöperation. The dog is a semi-gregarious animal. Men who love the music of self-praise will claim to have created his social virtues through domestication. The fact is, however, that many different kinds of wild animals, some of them far less intelligent than the dog, have repeatedly displayed comparable virtues. After observations have been sifted from the sentiments of the observers, enough evidence remains to warrant this conclusion. There is an undoubted though sporadically expressed tendency to sociability in animals as individuals which as species lack the tendency to form elaborate societies.

The general nature of this tendency may be illustrated by an incident reported by Kropotkin after a visit to the Brighton aquarium. A large Molucca crab had fallen on his back beneath an iron bar in the corner of a tank, and was struggling vainly to turn over. Other crabs came to the rescue. Again and again they tried to right their unfortunate comrade, only to be thwarted by the iron bar above him. After several attempts one member of the rescue crew would go to the bottom of .the tank for reënforcements, and the work would proceed with fresh vigor. The crabs were still at work after two hours when Kropotkin left the aquarium.

The literature of natural history is rich in such incidents.

The tendency for gregarious and semi-gregarious animals to be sociable is no more debatable than their tendency to quarrel, and it exists perhaps for as valid a biological reason. Just how it came to exist is more difficult to explain. The psychical sociability of gregarious creatures is so fundamentally different from the physical association of colonial creatures that the one cannot reasonably be presumed to have evolved from the other. And this is only part of the mystery of the origin of gregarious unions. There has been no noticeable evolution of a social instinct along the gregarious level itself.

It is impossible to construct such a functionally progressive series of types for the herd as Thomson and Geddes constructed for the colony. The occasional sociability of crabs today is not noticeably different from the occasional sociability of other gregarious animals. The social acts of such creatures in general are not demonstrably an elaboration of the social acts of their ancestors. For all that anyone knows to the contrary, they are Topsys that "just growed" out of some anonymous urge for coöperation.

v

The social insects are the simplest creatures that live in true societies. They constitute but a small percentage of the largest class of many-celled animals on earth. The geologist defies the imagination when he numbers the years of a geologic period, but no more so than does the biologist when he numbers the species of insects. L. O. Howard estimates that 3,500,000 different kinds of insects exist today. Could the extinct varieties be adequately estimated the total would be greatly increased. The swarm of grasshoppers that darkens the sun is only a fraction of one of these species. Should the biologist attempt to estimate the number of individuals in a single generation of grasshoppers alone, he would make the geologist blush.

Only three orders of insects contain any highly social species. Silverfish, cockroaches, locusts, lice, cicadas, caddis flies, butterflies, moths, fleas, ticks, and a good many other insects, have never developed far beyond mere gregariousness. It is a significant comment on the sporadic nature of the tendency toward coöperation that only the termites, the bees, the ants, and some of the wasps and beetles, have ever done that. It is a significant comment on the persistence of the tendency, however, that they have done it no fewer than twenty-four times in the course of their geologic history.

If life were as logical as the theories that aspire to explain it, the intricate harmony of the hive might well be an elaboration of the loose sociability of the swarm. But except that physically distinct individuals are involved in both cases, the swarm and the hive have very little in common today. For all that is known of yesterday they had no more in common then. Though originally all insects would seem to have been gregarious or semi-gregarious, the swarm was not demonstrably ancestral to the hive. For here again we find a difference of kind rather than of degree. True insect communities stand on a level of coöperation as distinct as the levels of the colony and the herd.

Despite its complexity in detail, the evolution of the insects was characterized in general by three significant events. These events were apparently impelled by three significant changes in environment. The first event was the origin of the insects, presumably a response to the origin of land vegetation. Stemming most likely from some primitive crustacean, insects were among the earliest creatures to develop a mechanism for breathing air. They rose to the land in the wake of the plants in the middle of the Paleozoic era. At its close they had radiated into many environments and had developed the diverse abilities of swimming, running, and flying. Not one species, however, could chirp, not one could eat anything but meat. Not one had developed a society.

Before the Paleozoic gave way to the Mesozoic era, the prevailingly mild moist climate gave way to drought, aridity, and glaciation. Under the lash of these adversities, insects took the second significant step in their evolution. Many of the primitive land plants perished, and with them many of the primitive insects. Not a few of the insects that emerged were remarkably modern. Among other things, they had come to practice that strange metamorphosis from grub to pupa to adult which is the greatest marvel of the modern insect, and one of the greatest marvels in the entire living world. The pupal stage of rest in this complicated cycle was probably a response to periodic inclemency of climate. It made possible an unprecedented diversity of form and adaptation, but it did not make possible the rise of a true society.

Not until after the appearance of the flowering plants toward the close of the Mesozoic era did the third significant event take place: the appearance of insects to eat the flowers. Among these were the first social insects, but why they were among them is purely a matter for conjecture. They are as socially different from other flower-eating insects as from their meat-eating ancestors. Their societies are a freak in the general evolution of insects rather than its inevitable culmination.

One thing, however, may be positively said about the evolution of insect societies. Every society that has ever been thoroughly studied—and there have been many—is founded on the family relationship. Concern for offspring rather than love of company is the rock on which each one rests.

The social insects, as we saw in the preceding chapter, are the simplest creatures to exhibit the mother instinct. They are also the simplest creatures to exhibit a truly social organization. The presumption is, therefore, strong that the mother instinct is the evolutionary parent of their social organization.

Some of the best writing in the field of natural history has been inspired by the social insects. Their fascinating and varied activities have been superbly described by Fabre, Maeterlinck, and Wheeler. It is not necessary to redescribe them here, but only to point out that they are made possible by maternal devotion and vigor. Nothing comparable to them exists among such insects as butterflies and May flies wherein the mother dies soon after laying her eggs. The typical community of social insects is established for the care of a numerous brood by a queen that may live as long as fifteen years. It endures as a society only so long as the queen and her successors endure as individuals.

From this root of maternal devotion and vigor there has grown a varied foliage of adaptations. Corporate activity, individual self-subordination, and division of labor exist in all types of insect societies, but social economies vary widely with the types. They grade from relative simplicity among all the beetles to extreme complexity among several varieties of termites, bees, and ants. There may be as many as eight distinct castes in a termite society, each devoted to a particular phase of working, fighting, or breeding; each as different from the others in appearance as in pursuit. But no matter how complicated the economy is, it revolves around the queen.

VI

Some observers have suggested that the different types of insect communities in the world today may epitomize the different stages through which the communal insects have evolved. They have carried their love of analogy so far as to suggest that ants and men may have traveled the same path of social evolution. The nomadic driver ants of Brazil live largely by raiding the establishments of other ants. It has been suggested that they may commemorate an early stage in the history of ants, comparable to an early stage of predatory savagery among men.

It is a short step from raiding for food to raiding for captives capable of producing food. Hoarded booty in the form of pupae and larvae will change in the natural course of events from food to food-producers. Its owners will change from marauders to slave-holders. Certain marauding ants have become so dependent on their slaves that they would starve without them. These ants, of which there are several species today, might be taken to epitomize a second stage in the social evolution of ants and men.

By the same sort of reasoning the herding ants that tend their aphids as men tend cows might represent a third stage. The harvesting ants that store seeds as men store crops might represent a fourth. To bring the analogy thoroughly to date the thieving ants might be added to illustrate a fifth. These racketeering ants, like racketeering humans, are less forthright than the out-and-out marauders. They build small galleries close to the large galleries of their victims and attack through inconspicuous avenues of approach. Being small and inconspicuous themselves, they can generally work among their rich and self-centered neighbors without detection. When occasionally they are found out, they can retreat to their dens through passageways too small to admit a pursuer.

Dear as this parable may be to the anthropomorphic sentiments of men, it is less appealing to their reason. Certain societies of ants and men may possibly have evolved through somewhat comparable marauding, herding, agricultural and racketeering stages, but it is not likely that all of them have. It is a safe guess that the history of ants and men was considerably more complicated than anyone can know or imagine.

Thus to analogize the evolution of ants and men is to indulge in an interesting but idle speculation. It is also to risk a misrepresentation. Though the associations of both are in a broad sense psychical, though they both may show corporate activity and individual self-subordination in a high degree, the one is fundamentally instinctive and the other intelligent. An ant society is as nearly perfect and automatic as a watch. A human society misses both perfection and automatism by wide margins.

To assume that the intelligent societies of men are closely related to the instinctive communities of insects is absurd. To assume that they are closely related to the only slightly less instinctive associations of most gregarious animals is only slightly less absurd. Men are genetically closer to a herd of cows than to a hive of bees, but they are sociologically far from both. Their coöperative behavior exists on its own level which is as distinct as the other levels that lie (in the opinion of men) beneath it.

A man need only look into himself or out at his fellows to see that the level is rather less "high" than it is generally presumed to be. The coöperative behavior of men very seldom extends beyond the borders of limited social groups. The outsiders are almost invariably viewed with suspicion by the insiders, and suspicion almost invariably leads to hostility.

This attitude had been summed up by one writer in a sentence. "In primitive culture there is a dual system of morals: the one of kindness, love, help, and peace, applicable to the members of our clan, tribe, or community; the other of robbery, enmity, and murder, to be practised against all the rest of the world; and the latter is regarded as quite as much a sacred duty as the former." It is hardly necessary to add that the phenomenon is not restricted to primitives. Moderns with their "Kamerads" and their "Heils" show only too loudly how men can love and hate their kind with equal ardor. This duality is obviously inconsistent with an unlimited instinctive love of man for man.

It is not inconsistent, on the other hand, with the limited instinctive love of men in family units. Men are creatures whose young are the most helpless on earth, and whose family organization as a result is the closest and most enduring union of its type on earth. Only the manlike apes approach men in this respect. Among these apes the normal social group is the family consisting of one strong male and a few females with their offspring. Many scientists believe that the normal social group among the ancestors of men was much the same.

They believe that the clan, the tribe, the state, and the federation of states are evolutionary extensions of the primitive family. Self-subordination of the individual to the group is, accordingly, an outgrowth from the jealous domination of the primitive father. Loyalty and altruism are outgrowths from the zealous care of the primitive mother. The hostility of one group to another is an outgrowth from the timidity and fear of the primitive child. Psychoanalysts use this theory to explain the origin of repressions and fixations among civilized men. Anthropologists use it to correlate the customs and tabus of a variety of contemporary peoples. In one form or another the theory is one of the most popular speculations of the day.

If it is true that human societies are rooted in the parental and filial instincts, they would appear to be similar in origin to the communities of social insects. But there are no known genetic connections between these instincts in social insects and men. There is not even a close connection between the human family and the civilized human society. Whatever their origin may have been, most human societies are obviously more opportunistic than instinctive today. They have apparently been so for a considerable length of time. Neither the human family nor the human state has undergone a uniform development the world around, or a consistent development in any particular race or tribe. Through the marvelous ingenuity of their minds men shift their social habits to meet demands. They are the most facile opportunists on earth.

Through their unprecedented power of adaptation, men have made their societies more varied and variable than any other type of corporate enterprise in the world. Through reason, memory, speech, and imagination, they have freed them from the standardization that freezes the unions of algae and ants. Through the unparalleled power of their minds, in short, men have become to an unparalleled degree the masters of their fate. Unfortunately, they have not invariably used the power of their intelligence intelligently. They have built the most futilely competitive as well as the most intricately coöperative associations in the world. How to decrease the one and to increase the other is today's most pressing problem—and tomorrow's most precious secret.

VII

So we complete our search for evidence of coöperation in the living world. No one can deny that the search has been successful. Coöperation is a widespread phenomenon in Nature. But how is the phenomenon related to the widespread phenomenon of conflict?

It is reasonable to assume that coöperative activity would be much less prevalent if it did not generally bestow very positive advantages on the creatures that practise it. It is unreasonable to assume, on the other hand, that the advantages may not be somewhat offset by disadvantages. As a matter of observable fact, coöperation is not invariably perfect as a way of life because Nature is not invariably perfect as an economist.

There are many sentimentalists to criticize the lives of other creatures by the ethical and aesthetic standards of men. There are many scientists to criticize the sentimentalists for being crudely egocentric. There are only a few philosophers to criticize the scientists for the tacit assumption that because other creatures cannot be correctly judged by human standards they cannot be judged at all.

Implicit in this assumption is the belief that the lives of all creatures but men are without direction. It is obvious, however, that if plants and animals had not tended on the whole toward safe and efficient ways of living, few would be living today. Safety and efficiency, accordingly, are valid standards by which to judge and compare them. By these standards coöperative relationships are not all equally good.

Individual freedom is the inevitable cost of coöperation, and in some cases the cost is too high. Drone bees, for example, are so specialized as gigolos that they are incapable of any other pursuit. They are unable to gather pollen because their tongues are too short. They are unable to work on the hive because they have no wax-glands. They are unable to fight because they have no stings. They would rather starve than collect food for themselves—and starve they frequently do. Dedicated exclusively to the business of being male, they even fail at that. Only one of

many succeeds in winning the queen, and that one dies as
he succeeds.

A drone's life is far from the ultimate in safety and efficiency for the individual. The economy of the drone caste
is far from the ultimate in safety and efficiency for the
group. With the opulence of high summer the drones are
no great burden, but when autumn begins to levy its tax
on the flowers the drones begin to levy theirs on the hive.
Short rations and dissension curse the community until
the drones are driven away.

Nor is the hive the only social institution that harbors
degeneration. Many a soldier termite has mandibles so
highly specialized for fighting that they are useless for
feeding. The honey ants of Texas are unable to manufacture jugs for storing food against periods of drought, so
some of them make jugs of themselves. They perform
this unusual feat extremely well, but at the expense of all
other activities. Hanging from the ceilings of their nests,
they receive the precious juice as the foragers bring it in,
until their bellies grow as bulbous as balloons. When
drought and hunger fall upon the hill, the workers stroke
the heads of the living jugs until the honey is milked out.

Loss of personal freedom and degeneration are not the
only dangers of coöperation, and social insects are not the
only creatures endangered. In more than one type of cooperative association, as men well know, the instinct to
protect and foster others is a boon to parasitism and disease.
In more than one instance, divisions of labor are so intimately enmeshed that if one cog slips the entire machine
may be wrecked. Nevertheless, when the debits against
coöperation are added, the credits more than balance them.

High on the credit side is the strength that union en-
genders. Countless species of small animals, which as indi-

viduals could find no surcease from danger and fear, as
groups find safety and peace. Food no creature could
obtain alone is easily obtained by creatures in organized
bands. Countless adaptations toward safer, easier, and
richer living are rooted in the tendency to coöperate.

Though irregularly and diversely developed today, these
adaptations contribute vastly to the fitness which makes
living possible. Though unevenly and discontinuously
evolved in the past, they must have contributed vastly to
the fitness which made survival possible. Though the tendency that produces them is erratic and mysterious in its
working, it yet works as certainly as the tendency that
makes for conflict.

It does so for very good reasons. An economy which
provides that the lions shall eat the lambs must also provide checks for the process if lions and lambs are not both
to become extinct. The most effective check is the balance
that Nature has arranged between the rapacity of the lions
and the fecundity of the lambs. The second most effective
check is coöperation among the lambs. If these two checks
had not been imposed upon the power of tooth and claw,
life would long since have vanished from the earth.

Coöperation, however, does more than help the feeble
to withstand the strong. It helps the feeble and the strong
alike to withstand the rigors of the physical environment.
It helps them to form new habits and to find new foods
and abodes—to increase their defenses on many fronts. It
is the flywheel that not only helps keep the machine of life
from tearing itself to pieces, but also helps keep it on the
road.

Chapter VIII

THE TRAGIC RHYTHM

LOVE makes the world go round, but it would not go long were it not for death which keeps the wheels from jamming. Only the unsexed and potentially immortal one-celled plants and animals escape the customary coercions of both death and love. The activity of these deities that mold the fate of living creatures is in general an inevitable procedure, even in man who thinks of himself as free. Though physicians and moralists may be loath to admit it, dying and loving can be deferred in time or altered in form but never wholly avoided.

After a fashion not uncommon among deities, death and love have ever fought for opposite ends. The one would level all life to the muck whence first it arose, the other would lift it higher toward the sky. Their battling in the blood of individuals has shaped the basic patterns of existence. Their warring in the blood of races has shaped the course of history.

Death, at first thought, would seem the stronger contender. Though love should win a decisive victory on any front, her legions would multiply to their own undoing and in their very triumph find defeat. Then, too, such a solar calamity as originally made possible the earth and its life might some day return to destroy them. There is, fortunately, no immediate prospect of so violent a victory for death. The campaign is more apt to go into the future as it has come from the past—with offense and defense essentially in balance. Death will doubtless continue to destroy individuals as well as races, and love will doubtless continue to replace them.

A life when not too closely examined is a simple thing: a borrowed handful of muck from the earth, shaped for a time by a few ergs of energy and then returned. Races tend to be little different. Like individuals they are born to mature, to grow old, and eventually to die. The only essential difference between the two cycles is that the one may be slow in unrolling, and the other must be fast.

When a man grows old he loses his teeth and his tolerance for the ways of youth. When prehistoric races grew old, many of them likewise lost their teeth if not their tolerance. In those days there were no dentists to fill cavities or to scrape out the rot of pyorrhea, but that would seem not to have been the reason why all members of certain species lost their teeth. Certain species of dinosaurs, for example, first lost their teeth and then their lives. They were obviously old and spent, and toothlessness was merely a manifestation of senility. Similarly, the nearly toothless state of modern egg-laying mammals and anteaters is a sign of the racial death that is growing within them.

Atrophy of such organs as teeth, which ironically imparts to the aged the seeming of youth without its substance, is not the only prophecy of extinction. Second childhood may be expressed in a fresh exuberance of vital power, but an exuberance without control. Just as the growth force of an aging individual may run amuck in a cancer, the growth force of an aging race may quicken to a lethal frenzy.

Spines and horns, for example, have always embellished the animal kingdom. They have generally been considered a response to the need for protection or an aid to amatory achievement. Though in many cases they have doubtless served both as instruments of coercion and ornaments of persuasion, their deeper meaning pertains more to death than to life. Bucks will tangle antlers in a forest brawl, but it is not through antlers that victory is won. Every hunter knows that a deer's most telling weapons are his feet. The antlers may even be a snare for death, as the starved carcasses of those that could not break clean from their clinches amply attest.

History reveals that the antlers of deer as well as the comparable adornments of other creatures have more than an accidental affiliation with death. They are one of the best indications of old age in a race. The Irish elk of the last glacial epoch stood eight feet high at the withers, and was unquestionably the handsomest member of the deer family that ever lived. But his magnificence was also his undoing. His twelve foot spread of antlers was not only a clumsy burden in the struggle for existence but a reflection of the last brave flicker in the vitality of his line. Today the Irish elk is dead without issue, skewered on his own antlers.

So too have fared many others. Several long lines of Paleozoic shellfish came to the end of undistinguished careers in a burst of spines. The finbacked reptiles of the Permian swamps were square-rigged ships whose port was extinction. One dinosaur of the Jurassic period was as impregnable as the Rock of Gibraltar, but the massive spines and plates that routed his outer enemies were powerless to forestall the inner death of which they were emblematic. By such tokens as these the horned toads and hedgehogs of today are surely doomed.

Abnormal size, like spinescence, is a prophecy of extinction. When a man grows greatly beyond the average size of men, he may earn his living in a side show—but he will probably not have to labor long. When all members of a species grow noticeably larger than the members of re-

lated species, the race is similarly tabbed for an early end.
Nature has many times enacted the fable of the frog that
tried to rival the ox. The battlefields of time are strewn
with the bones of giants.

Brachiopods are the most modest of shellfish. They generally stop growing when they have reached the width of
an inch or two. One Paleozoic species, however, achieved
the width of a foot. It was by far the largest of its line,
but it paid for the distinction by being also the last. The
greatest carnivorous as well as the greatest herbivorous
dinosaurs of the Mesozoic era immediately preceded the
extinction of their kind. The largest invertebrate animal
that ever lived is a fifty foot squid; the largest known vertebrates are the whales. Both are alive today, but their pros-
pects for tomorrow are poor. Similarly, the hippopotamus
and the gorilla are rapidly failing while smaller pigs and
primates carry on. By maturing more leisurely and reproducing more modestly than their lesser kin, the giant species
move slowly but inexorably toward the grave.

II

Though it would seem to be "normal" for races to grow
slowly old and die, senescence is not demonstrably a cause
of death. It is merely in some cases a part of the process
of death. In other cases it is not even part of the process.
Death is impatient, and frequently stops the show before
senescence can herald the end. Just as an individual may die
before his time, so may a race. Indeed, because most prehistoric races disappeared before old age had placed its
certain marks upon them, one is forced to seek elsewhere
for the causes of their passing.

Among the unpredictable hazards that may stop short
the cycle of an individual life, disease is perhaps the most

ominous. It is the most poisonous snake in the grass of terrestrial bliss. It has harassed mankind from the beginning, sometimes feeding fastidiously on selected victims, sometimes striking with undiscriminative abandon at an entire race. During the fourteenth century, in the guise of the Black Death, it precipitated the greatest calamity in human history. It laid low well-nigh the entire population of Europe, of which one-fourth, some twenty-five million men and women, never rose again. Had its virulence been only a little greater, the Black Death and its henchman, famine, might well have exterminated all.

No paleontologist can read the tragic history of disease among the most resourceful animals of today without wondering if their less endowed forbears of yesterday may not have suffered similarly. One even wonders if disease may not have been one of the causes of extinction. Unfortunately, most maladies attack the soft tissues, and the soft tissues of most fossils are lost. Yet facts concerning the history of ancient distempers have been accumulating for one hundred and fifty years. They tell an interesting and a surprising story.

The first intimation that all had not always been well with the health of prehistoric beasts came in 1774 from Professor Esper of Erlangen. He described a lesion on the thigh bone of an extinct cave bear as a cancer, which later scholars have identified as the scar of an infected fracture. In the early decades of the nineteenth century, Goldfuss, Cuvier, and von Walther described many similar lesions on the remains of other mammals from the Pleistocene interglacial formations. It becomes apparent that bacteria were busy then as now, but also that their activities were probably less dangerous than annoying. In only a few recorded cases did they kill an individual, and there is no evidence that they ever threatened a race.

Later investigations of Virchow, Mayer, Moodie, and others reached deeper into the past, only to substantiate the original findings. They unearthed the unhappy evidence of a three-toed horse with pyorrhea; of a dinosaur with a leg abscess capable of holding a tubful of pus; of an ancestral reptile with inflammation of the spine; of a mosasaur with gout. They discovered ulcerous teeth, rheumatic joints and tubercular bones. But they found nothing which conceivably might have brought whole species to their doom.

They found, on the contrary, a strange divorcement of disease and racial death. In the beginning, when creatures embraced one another less intimately than they do today, many a modern malady was unknown. Half of geologic time had slipped away before communalism gave birth to parasitism, and parasitism to disease. Yet death did not wait for society to sour. Long before disease had riddled the flesh, a host of species had come and gone. Whole dynasties like that of the trilobites had endured for immeasurable eons untainted by disease, and had died as clean as they had lived.

Bacterial epidemics, to be sure, may have harassed the beasts of the past without leaving on their bones any scars of certain proof. The rise in the Tertiary period of such modern insects as the tsetse fly suggests this possibility. But it is not likely that epidemic disease ever felled an entire species. A few individuals at least might reasonably be assumed to have escaped, and a few would have been enough to rehabilitate the race. The effect of pestilence on a race is not death but immunity. Men, who live even more closely in their cities than do bees in their hives (and far more filthily and unhealthily), would long since have disappeared if this were not true.

Disease, in short, is impotent against that vital force

which has quickened the streams of flesh through time. Extinction must lie largely in the failure of that force to prevent the channels from clogging in a troubled world.

III

There are several ways of dealing with difficulties too stern to be wholly mastered. One is to face them bravely in the manner of the Light Brigade, and needlessly succumb. Another is to deny their existence, as some people deny their diseases, but to die of them nevertheless. Yet another is to find a haven far from the madding crowd's ignoble strife, and like monks in their cells exchange the wear of war for the rust of peace. The proved best, however, is to compromise, and by giving way a little prevent being swept away entirely.

Most of these expedients are older than man, and were abundantly tested long before his coming. The woolly mammoth of the last glacial epoch strove against the ice only to perish, as it were, in a plethora of bravado. Many an ancient shellfish buried itself in mud remote from the centers of conflict, only to exchange the possibility of a violent death for the certainty of a degenerate life. But most creatures of the past, like most men today, arrived at a compromise with fate. Their ability to do so was their saving grace.

Acquired immunity to disease is but one example of the ability of flesh to compromise—of what biologists call its adaptability. Other examples everywhere meet the eye. Bacteria, for instance, can live on sulphur, horses on hay, Eskimos on blubber, and civilized man apparently on anything that happens to be in style. Moles dwell in the ground, fish in the water, and birds in the air. The Tibetan is reasonably happy three miles above the level of the sea, the Imperial Valley farmer two hundred feet below it; the Javanese in the endless dog days of the tropics, the Laplander in the endless frost of the tundras; the Arab under a rainfall of less than five inches per year, the Malay under more than two hundred. The flesh from which all were fashioned is apparently as adjustable as rubber.

Like rubber, however, it snaps when stressed beyond its strength. The man who made his living in buggy whips before automobile accelerators replaced them, today makes only an unhappy illustration of a problem as old as time. The world is constantly changing and creatures must change in accordance. Generally, the creatures that succeed most admirably in their adjustments fail most miserably when they are forced to change them. Nothing can fail like success.

Success consists in the ability to shape oneself for the life one is forced to lead. During the World War a little sign hung in the practice trenches on Parris Island, where the "boots" of the United States Marine Corps were attempting to master the art of the bayonet. It instilled in the students a hunger for learning uncommon among men, for it reminded them that "if you don't learn you die." Civilized men, whose mistakes are not generally deadly, had a taste of the technique whereby Nature has taught her less privileged children for eons.

One can see how effective this technique may be by watching the gibbons in a tropical wood so deftly defying death as they swing from branch to branch, clearing as much as forty feet in a swing; never failing to estimate instantaneously and correctly the strength and distance of each new objective and the energy necessary to reach it. Gibbons are the finest acrobats on earth because for ages the only net beneath them was the grave.

Gibbons afoot, however, are waddling cripples easily

overtaken by men. Should the forest fail, their plight on the ground is easy to imagine. The very qualities that make them succeed in the trees would make them succumb if the trees were taken away. Such is the curse of rigidity in a flexible world. Its ominous shadow has darkened the paths of achievement from the beginning.

Dedicated to one way of life, an evolutionary line cannot ordinarily shift to a different life. It must proceed down the blind alley of its specialization until it can proceed no further. There, rigid in its perfection, it may only await the death which generally comes when new environment renders old adjustments useless.

Nature is hardly the sweet old lady that Victorian poetry has made her. She resembles more closely a paranoiac fiend who tricks to death her most distinguished children. The past is littered with the remains of those who carried all their bones in the basket of one adaptation. Only the relatively simple in structure and flexible in habit were able to weather the crises of geologic history. To them alone were born the new species that varied and preserved the flesh through the vicissitudes of a billion years.

IV

Racial failure is the complement of racial success, as night is the complement of day. Both are mysteries which no theory convincingly explains. By the theory of natural selection, which is the best documented explanation to date, both are the offspring of chance. Geneticists have delved deeply in the germ plasm of living organisms and have found it a sort of Roman candle whose variegated effusions they call mutations. Just as certain balls of a Roman candle travel farther, longer, and more brightly than others before they burn themselves out in the air, the mutants of a

species that happen best to fit their environment are presumed by the theory of natural selection to endure while
others die.

So far as such highly specialized animals as pigeons, dogs,
and horses are concerned, it would seem that the power of
the germ plasm to throw off mutations does not diminish
significantly with specialization. By artificial selection man
has played god to the multitudinous mutants of these creatures, choosing such types as pleased his fancy and from
them creating new varieties. The specialized dinosaurs and
pterodactyls of the past are presumed to have been no less
productive of mutations. They died without issue, not
because their germ plasm lost its inventiveness, but because
their mutations were somehow unable to get a footing at
a time when new environments made new adjustments
necessary for survival.

The rise of the hoofed mammals during the Tertiary
period was a mass movement toward specialization. When
grass began to grow on the treeless uplands at the beginning
of that period, hordes of browsing creatures came into the
open to graze. Their nondescript anatomy shaped with
time to the recognizable forms of camels, horses, and many
other grassland familiars of today. Slowly their teeth became better and better adapted to the grass, their bodies
and limbs to running over the land. Presumably, natural
selection saw to it that only those mutants prospered whose
teeth and limbs had happened to vary toward greater
efficiency in the specialized pursuits of pasture life.

The families that best adjusted themselves to the upland
environment were the least apt to profit from any mutations
that were not in the direct line of their specialization. Once
the horses had definitely become grazing and running animals, any deviation from specialized grazing teeth and running limbs would have been decidedly disadvantageous. A

horse with a lion's teeth but without a lion's love of meat would have been a mistake, and would have paid for the mistake with his life. A horse with an elephant's bulk, but without an elephant's jungle storehouse and retreat, would quickly have succumbed to his own or his enemy's hunger.

Hyohippus, indeed, would seem to have been an actual example of such an ill-starred horse. His teeth became specialized for browsing on the leaves of trees at a time when the trees were shriveling away in drought. While other horses followed the grasses to success, Hyohippus followed the trees to extinction. Should the grasses disappear from the prairie and the trees return, the grazers would presumably follow Hyohippus.

This explanation of extinction has so much impressive evidence and opinion in its favor that the cases to which it cannot apply are apt to be overlooked. Yet these cases are interesting and possibly significant. They at least suggest that the mechanics of evolution may just possibly be less simple and arbitrary than the theories which men have invented to explain them.

Not all the specialized creatures of the past succumbed when their environments changed because not every evolutionary sequence adhered consistently to the line of its original development. The sea-going porpoises and whales, for example, were once specialized for living on the land. They successfully shifted to a totally different environment and way of life. Geologic history supplies other examples of such radical changes in the direction of evolution. Unfortunately, it does not explain why some creatures were forced to follow the road of their original specializations to the grave while others were able to detour.

Natural selection is widely assumed to be the one great conservative force in Nature which holds the radical variability of the germ plasm to straight and narrow paths. Yet if such creatures as whales could change their ways of living, presumably because of some relaxation in the vigilance of selection, might not other creatures conceivably have failed to change their ways of living because of some limitation on their variability? If selection can sometimes lose its rigidity and turn radical, is it not reasonable to suspect that variation can sometimes lose its flexibility and turn conservative?

There are, indeed, both experimental and historical facts to support this suspicion. Horticulturists have tried for centuries to develop blue roses, yellow sweet peas, and black tulips, but without success. Similarly, no mollusc has ever been known to grow a horny skeleton, no insect to grow any other kind. No hen has ever boasted the trunk and trumpet of an elephant, no elephant the comb and cackle of a hen. Such limitations are obviously imposed internally on the variability of species and not externally by selection.

The history of life as it is known through fossils abounds in evolutionary sequences which seem to have been directed at least in part by some guiding inner principle. Some of these sequences involved millions of years and scores of species. Most of them moved towards better and better adjustments for life, but a few of them seem to have headed for death from the start.

Certain long lines of fossil shellfish show progressive development of characters which could have had no imaginable survival value. Others show positively lethal trends. In one group of molluscs, for example, the apertures of the shells became more and more constricted with time until the animals were almost literally buried alive in their own external skeletons. Similarly, the backboned amblypods of the Eocene epoch evolved, as it were, deliberately towards extinction. While neighbors and relatives were growing more fleet and intelligent, the amblypods grew heavier and duller until finally they stumbled into the grave.

Such creatures moved to the end of their evolutionary careers before natural selection caught up with them to strike a telling blow. They evolved without giving off any mutations that enabled them to swerve from their deadly lines of march. What, exactly, was it that held them to these lines of march? It would be absurd to assume that natural selection steered their courses. It would be heretical in the opinion of science to assume that some mythical drive impelled them on their way. It would be profane in the opinion of religion to assume that this drive was suicidal. The student of fossils, accordingly, can choose between absurdity, heresy, and profanity in explaining them. Or he can conclude that death like life is an enigma which neither science nor religion has solved.

v

Whatever may be the true nature of the death with which all life is loaded, environment is certainly the trigger that has frequently set it off. Races do not just sink into the grave under the burden of their years, their ailments, or their rigidity. They must be kicked there by some outward force.

The most intimate environmental relationships of living creatures are those that living creatures impose upon one another. Though the crowding, brawling, cheating drive of life was wondrously arranged for a maximum of individual and a minimum of racial danger, fundamental derangements sometimes occur. Just as in Boston when the policemen went on strike and hoodlums destroyed in an hour a social equilibrium that had been fundamentally stable for a century, the associations of lesser animals may occasionally lose their balance. Powder long unused abruptly explodes with damage that may spread to racial proportion.

Man has many times demonstrated with his own clumsy fingers the hair trigger adjustments of the plant and animal worlds. He introduced the English sparrow to save the elms of New England from measuring worms. The sparrows, it must be admitted, did what was expected of them. But like all thorough-going reformers, they refused to cease their activities when their activities ceased being beneficial. They turned upon the native songbirds, driving them out of the villages throughout the United States, and doubtless decimating the less aggressive species. Man has more recently allayed this curse upon his inadvertence by replacing (again inadvertently) the droppings of horses with the fumes of automobiles. Possibly in this fashion he may ultimately exterminate the sparrows—provided, of course, he does not first exterminate himself.

Among all the aliens who have insinuated themselves into the United States, the gypsy- and brown-tailed moths are perhaps the least desirable. There was a time when it seemed that these two blackguards might destroy every shade and fruit tree in the land. Several decades have already passed in the attempt to curtail their depredations, but they are still a national problem. Similarly, the mongoose who was brought into Jamaica to kill rats remained hungry after the last rat had been eaten. He then advanced upon the birds and lizards with such eminent success that the insects which were normally restrained by these animals could stage a Roman holiday. Like a stone dropped into a quiet pool the mongoose was dropped into Jamaica, and the circle of disturbance spread through the life of the island from shore to shore.

Since the very beginning of human history man has dis-

turbed the established balance of Nature by shifting creatures from one habitat to another. When ancient man
brought the dingo dog of Asia to Australia, the native
marsupial "wolves" were doomed. Because she had been
built to carry her young in an abdominal pouch, the female
marsupial was sorely handicapped in repelling the attacks
of the invader; and when she perished in the attempt, her
babies perished with her. It is not surprising to read in the
rocks that the dingo triumphed completely in a trice of
geologic time.

Such happenings suggest the possibility of similar ones
before the coming of man. Examination of the geologic
record proves it. At the beginning of the Paleozoic era,
for example, hordes of tranquil creatures peopled the
tranquil seas. Invertebrate animals of many varieties bred
and basked in the warmth of a friendly world, content on
the whole to be soft and unambitious in a soft and un-
stimulating environment. But trouble was gathering in the
offing, in the streams of the land where fishes were sharpen-
ing their teeth on sterner problems. Agile, fertile, and
strong, they embodied what men call progress; and when
eventually they went to the sea in search of richer pastures,
they easily mastered the placid conservatives who lived
there. They not only contributed to the demise of many a
gentle sluggard, but they altered the entire plan of evolution.

Long, indeed, before the love of adventure and discontent bred wanderlust in the spirit of man, creatures of many
varieties and in many ages roamed the globe. Necessity
rather than whim was the force that set them journeying,
the unremitting need to eat and to be safe in a fickle world.
Generally beneath their restlessness has been the restlessness of Earth. Slowly shrinking these many eons, her surface has slowly cracked and wrinkled to fit the measure of a

diminishing core. Lands have flowed from form to form like clouds across the sky, forever fluxing in outline and relief; now low and vastly invaded by the hungry sea, now high and broad and triumphant. To the beat of this basic rhythm, earth's puny sucklings were shifted from teat to teat, and their fates were shifted in accordance.

The removal of physical barriers has frequently induced migration and consequent disturbance of the social balance. During the Pleistocene glacial period the writhing of the earth threw a bridge of land from North to South America. The saber-toothed cats, as though freed from a cage, moved quickly from the northern to the southern continent. They found what they sought in the person of the giant sloths, which in turn found relief from the burden of their unwieldy bodies.

The prevention of migratory movements through the establishment of barriers, especially water barriers, has also frequently disturbed the social balance. Protected from foreign invasion, the imprisoned animals have increased beyond the capacity of the land to sustain them, and death has stepped in to claim the weak. The bones of dwarfed Pleistocene elephants that had been trapped on islands in the Mediterranean attest the ruthlessness of the process. So, too, do the hard bitten ponies of the Shetland Islands which somehow survived a similar ordeal. But Nature is not consistent. The egg-laying mammals of Australia and the three-eyed lizards of New Zealand are anachronisms saved from a discarded society. Safe in their island strongholds they escaped the competition of the outer world which destroyed their kin. That one creature's meat shall be another creature's poison is a truth far older than man.

Indirectly, too, and even more profoundly do the spasms of earth affect the fate of the living. A continent tilts and new-born streams rush out of the highlands, draining en route the lowland swamps and killing the creatures that inhabit them. Pouring out mud and fresh water from their mouths they poison and choke the more delicate organisms of the sea. Or rising ranges of mountains disturb aerial currents so that climates are altered, and with them the lives of animals and plants. When desert, flood, or glacier seek the earth, the old, the weak, and the rigid find the grave.

The critical periods in terrestrial history, when the globe gave way to long stored stresses of shrinkage, were also the critical periods in the history of life. It was then that undistinguished races found their strength. It was then that races which had ruled for an eon vanished, as it were, in a night—their bones their only offspring. But why a few individuals of the ill-starred tribes did not somehow manage to escape and carry on, is a problem without a satisfying answer.

It only reminds us again that, despite our knowledge of death as a process, death as a principle is quite as mysterious as life. There is no more fundamental reason for dying than for living. Our knowledge of both concerns only the mechanisms and circumstances of their operation, not why they operate nor what they are. We only know that, ponder and fret and tinker as we may, the one is impossible without the other. Perhaps it is better so. For who shall say that life with its somber edging of death would be more beautiful in another frame?

Chapter IX

THE BUSINESS OF GROWING UP

Where within this frame of frustration does progress lie? How, without taking mankind for its goal and the standards of men for its measure, may a man define it? The libraries are full of attempts to answer these questions. But where in a wilderness of opinions is the truth? Where merely is one compelling opinion?

Many scientists seek the objective facts of Nature and let the meanings escape. Many philosophers seek the meanings without reference to the objective facts. Both call what they find The Truth. It is only, however, when the two techniques are combined that the result appeals to an intelligent layman's instinct for reality. Fortunately with regard to the problem of progress, such a combination has been tried. The result is the concept of emergent evolution.

When two atoms of hydrogen unite with one atom of oxygen, the result is not merely the sum of the properties of hydrogen and oxygen. The result is water with properties of its own. Similarly when a horse and an ass unite, the result is a mule which is different from both its parents. It is inevitable that such combinations shall continually occur in a continuously fluxing world, and that they shall possess new and unpredictable qualities. Recognition of this inevitability is the foundation of the concept of emergent evolution.

Mere newness, of course, is not progress. A two-headed cow is different from its one-headed parents, but inasmuch as its extra head confers no extra advantages for a bovine life the novelty is not progressive. No change is progressive unless the new extends the functional capabilities of the old. The doctrine of emergent evolution postulates that both the earth and its inhabitants have evolved in general toward greater and greater functional capability.

The simple gases out of which the solid earth is believed to have evolved were functionally more restricted than the simple compounds which are believed to have first resulted from their union. These compounds were functionally more restricted than the complex carbon compounds which are believed to have next appeared. The carbon compounds in their turn were functionally more restricted than the living cells which presumably came next. Similarly in the evolution of life through time, more widely functioning aggregates of cells evolved successively from less widely functioning aggregates. Evolution has been in general a process of creative synthesis.

So large and diversified a body of evidence supports this concept of emergent evolution that many of the best modern thinkers have accepted it in one or another of its many phases. It is the fundamental belief of Lloyd Morgan, who is responsible for its name, and of J. C. Smuts who calls it holism. It appears with varying extent in the writings of Whitehead, Alexander, Dewey, Woodbridge, Santayana, Boodin, Sellars, Spaulding, Montague, and a host of lesser philosophers. Such eminent scientists as Thomson, Geddes, and Jennings have also embraced it with enthusiasm. According to Professor Jennings it is "the declaration of independence of biology" which freed the sciences of life from the fetters of unimaginative materialism.

At this point the unreconstructed mechanists will rise in wrath. They will say that emergent evolution is just another name for Aristotle's "internal perfecting tendency," Schopenhauer's "will," Driesch's "entelechy," and Bergson's "élan vital." They will say that like these earlier concepts it rests on the assumption of a force which transcends the known limits of physical and chemical laws. For this objection, however, the shells and bones of extinct creatures have a peculiarly effective rebuttal.

No one can rightly deny that environment has repeatedly limited and stereotyped the adjustments of living creatures. No one can rightly deny that as a result many cycles of evolution have been discontinuous and repetitious. It is obvious, however, that not all the cycles could have been wholly so because life would then be the same today as it was a billion years ago.

A superficial scrutiny of the geologic record will suffice to show that not all comparable adaptations of living creatures have been comparably effective. The mammals, for example, made adjustments to the same environments that the reptiles had occupied before them. Beginning as localized and generalized types, they radiated into every environment and became the specialized horses, dogs, moles, whales, bats, and monkeys of today. Though the reptiles had undergone a comparable radiation in an earlier era, the mammals did not merely duplicate the adaptations of the reptiles. In many points of efficiency and safety they bettered them.

Despite repetition in a multitude of minor trends, the major trends of organic history have been similarly progressive. During the more remote periods of geologic time, organisms were in general more primitive than they are today. Adaptations and anatomy became in general increasingly diversified and complex. The deployment of a simple primordial society from the monotonous primordial environment of the sea was like the advance of a conquering army. Like such an army life won decisive battles on several fronts. These victories were truly progressive because they not only extended the range of life to the ends of the earth but they increased the efficiency and safety of living there.

From the point of view of a perfectly ordered economy, the known methods of achieving these ends could hardly be called efficient and safe. It would be difficult to imagine more wasteful devices for extending the range and improving the adaptations of living creatures than random variation and selection. It would be difficult to imagine any form of stagnation, degeneracy, or death which the geologic record does not amply record. Indeed, the greatest mystery of a billion years of living is that when its losses and gains are evaluated there should be a balance in favor of the gains. That there have been more gains than losses is apparent when we strip the geological story of life to the skeleton of its plot.

II

Plants, which were destined to perform the humbler tasks in the warfare of living, performed them at first quite humbly indeed. History, in fact, has all but forgotten that they performed at all. The fog that shrouds the plants of Pre-Cambrian time shrouds also those of many a subsequent eon. Only after animals had filled more than half the annals of the Paleozoic era with their exploits did their lesser companions begin in real earnest to record their exploits too.

Inconspicuous though they were through much of their history, plants were yet indispensable. Beneath the insurgent adventuring of the animal is the torpid complacency of the plant. For with sunfire and clod the plant builds sugar and starch, fuels which alone can stoke the furnace of animal vitality. No animal can make these fuels for himself. Today and on every remembered day of the past, animals are and have been parasites on plants.

So it is that though the record of vegetation in the more distant past is slight and vague, plants too small and soft for preservation were doubtless performing their functions then as now. Then, perhaps even more copiously than now, these lesser members of a lesser tribe were doubtless swarming in the brine and ooze of the sea. Individually insignificant but collectively invaluable, their legions must have marched in the campaign of more illustrious compatriots against a hostile world.

Some of these primitive plants secreted stony skeletons, and left a definite record of their lives. Their story, however, is doubtless the story of a few among many. Practically all of the fungi, most complex and varied group of primitive plants in the world today, came out of an unknown past; most of the members of the better recorded lesser groups are largely unrecorded. Scattered and smeared by the winds of time, the library of their early lives will never be assembled.

The present, however, reveals not a little of the past. The simple water plants of the modern earth are the simplest things alive; no organism could ever conceivably have been more primitive than some of them. They suggest a time when all creatures lay listless in the sea. Few possess differentiated organs such as stem and leaf; few are able to nourish themselves or even to support their own weight on land. All are anachronisms in the modern world. While others were moving toward better adjustments in a million walks of living, the bacteria, algae, fungi, and their kin merely lived.

Despite all this they are of prime importance in the drama of living. Closest of all creatures to the crude inorganic necessities of life, they are ablest in preparing these necessities for general and continued use. Without their services the so-called higher organisms would disappear as surely as without them they would never have originally appeared. The primitive plants, in fact, are the very foundation of the living world. They constitute the first great triumph of the vegetable kingdom, first in significance no less than in time.

It is likely that every advance in the history of life was really a retreat. For every well documented advance was prodded along by the bayonet of death. Thus doubtless did Nature evolve the first plants that were capable of living on land. Love of the new and the dangerous experience has never been a noticeable part of the vegetable temperament. So long as water was plentiful, no plant would ever have left it. Only those plants that had clung to the unreliable bosom of lakes and streams ever had any reason for leaving it.

Drought fell frequently on ancient lands, and countless lake and river plants must have vanished with the water. Those alone whose cuticle was exceptionally tough, and whose bodies were able to suck moisture from the soil, could possibly have survived. Through an untold number of harassed generations the strong found mates while the weak found only extinction. In time the fortunates that survived could no doubt take their food as readily from air as from water. And so, as is Nature's way with both race and individual, a new thing was born in travail to the earth.

While the simple backboneless animals of the sea were writing the story of their golden age, the pioneer plants of the land were quietly preparing for theirs. Within the limits that Nature had early decreed they were struggling, however unconsciously, toward greater efficiency and safety. They were beginning to stretch green leaves to the sun above and roots to the soil below, achieving thereby a far more effective capture and conversion of food and drink. They were beginning to lift their prostrate bodies off the ground on stems which were bundles of thick-walled woody tubes. Through these as through pipes the food and water were kept in constant and effective circulation. And through these, at last, the plants of the land began to write their history in the rocks.

When the backboned fishes had come with the Devonian period to rule the seas, the woody plants had also come to rule the lands. In a middle Devonian formation near Rhynie, Scotland, one of the oldest known forests on earth is well preserved. Though the wood was spongy and the foliage sparse, some of the trees reached a height of thirty or forty feet. And though their low-born origin was deeply stamped on great and small alike, the promise of a richer future was stamped there too.

The vegetable streamer of the rocket of life, which so long had traveled so dimly, was sputtering with the start of a mighty explosion. The explosion came toward the close of the era, in the period called Pennsylvanian. On a stage of far-flung marshlands in every continent of the world, the minor actors in the drama of life ran away with the show. Ferns and rushes of prodigious size lifted their heads in the air, while at their feet a multitude of smaller growths lay wantonly intertwined. The first real heyday in the history of plants had come at last, and each in its own favored fashion made the most of it.

Nature was kind in many ways to these and to others like them. She gave them a warm, damp world of vast extent, a world exactly suited to their needs. Two things, however, she withheld. She reserved for others the flowers and the seeds which enabled them to escape from the swamps.

Nature had altered the mechanism of reproduction in plants with every major alteration of anatomy until in the ferns and their relatives it had grown absurdly complex.

The lordly rulers of the Paleozoic swamps were also the slaves of a clumsy compromise. During most of their lives they lived quite innocent of sex. Maturing, however, they gave rise to spores which grew, if they settled on spots of sufficient moisture, into drab little plants with male and female organs. Because the spores could only sprout in soggy ground and the sperms could only reach the eggs by swimming, the Paleozoic giants could never stray far from the water. It was Nature's jest to the spore-bearers that they be held so securely by so slight a chain so far from any real triumph on the land.

Improvements in living for both plants and animals have ever been geared to the mechanism of reproduction. Haphazard marriage of egg and sperm in the shifty and dangerous medium of water is a curse on the ferns. It is also a curse on the fishes. Both are born only by a lucky chance, and by a lucky chance alone can either survive the trials of early youth.

It took nearly a billion years to evolve devices for restricting sex to the inner privacy of those that possess it, and it may take a billion more to apply them to any considerable percentage of living creatures. It took nearly a billion years to perfect machinery for strengthening the young in the bodies of their mothers before they are thrown on the doubtful mercy of the world. Ferns and fishes arrived too early to receive the blessings destined in the future to enrich the lives of maples and men.

These blessings came to animals by way of the placenta and to plants by way of flower and seed. In both the mammals and the flowering plants, the act of fertilization is effected with some efficiency; not, to be sure, without the chance of failure in individual cases, but with a great reduction of that chance so far as the species is concerned. In both, the embryos are nourished within the body of

the mother to a stage of relative maturity before they are
born. For both, the ancient tyranny of water is mollified
to a great extent.

Flowers are the sexual organs of the plants they adorn,
and they contain both male and female organs. Their business is to get fertilized and produce seeds. Because most
plants have been compelled to sit in chains while most animals roam, a third party must inevitably assist in the act
of bisexual reproduction. All the grasses, as well as such
cone-bearing trees as the pines and the hemlocks, are fertilized by the wind. Though wind is a more reliable inter-
mediary than water, it is not a perfect one. Enormous
quantities of the sperm-bearing pollen must be produced
to allow for that which fails of its destination. More efficient is cross-pollination by insects, a method used by all
elaborately flowered plants. The insects do not work for
nothing, to be sure, but they are far less expensive than the
undirected forces of the physical world.

In the seed which grows from the fertilized flower the
plant gets a start in life. When the seed plants first appeared in the fossil record of Devonian times, they were
already well established in the citizenry of terrestrial vegetation. But desert, cold, and convulsion gripped the earth
at the close of the Paleozoic era, all but exterminating the
denizens of the swamps. Most of the spore-bearers vanished with the water, and those that managed to survive
were forever shorn of their glory. Most of the seed plants
vanished too, but not before they had mothered the cycads.

By the Jurassic period of the Mesozoic era these plants
which resemble both the palms and the ferns had risen to
rule the vegetable world. More than half the known plants
of the age were cycads, and most of the rest were primitive
cone-bearing relatives. All were distinguished by the lack
of distinguished flowers. All had seeds that grew no armor

to protect the embryos within, a weakness which held them short of the ultimate victory of the vegetable kingdom.

This victory was reserved for the more elaborately flowered hardwood trees and their numerous kin. Last of the great vegetable clans to appear on earth, they were first to achieve the perfection which had been foreshadowed in the earliest seed ferns. In them alone is the promise of the seed made real. For safe with a safety no other plant has ever enjoyed, in a tiny fortress well stocked with food and drink, each embryonic growth is toughened to meet the dangers of its early life.

Successful from their first appearance toward the close of the Mesozoic era, these plants possess the lands today. They constitute three-fourths of all existing vegetable species, exclusive of bacteria and fungi. It is largely they that mantle the earth with green, that venture highest on the mountains and farthest on the desert wastes. It is they alone among plants of the land that challenge the supremacy of algae in the water.

Yet even these are shadowed by a cloud. Though blessed with beauty and power beyond any of their kin, they must yet abide by the ancient decree which holds all plants to menial tasks. Quietly sitting in the sun, they store the energy of air and earth for animals to squander.

III

The history of animals like that of plants does not begin at the beginning. Animals were already a success before Nature vouchsafed any fulsome account of them in the rocks. The oldest abundant fossil remains occur in Cambrian formations throughout the world, and they show how diversified and complex the adaptations and anatomy of animals had already become. Animals, indeed, had already mastered the sea.

Sponges were the least pretentious citizens of that ancient society, yet even they had acquired a variety of body styles to fit a variety of marine conditions. They had acquired simple but adequate mechanisms for reproducing, and for capturing food and expelling waste. Jellyfishes and their relatives had developed tentaculated mouths and digestive cavities for furthering nutrition among themselves, and a battery of stinging cells for retarding it among their neighbors. They had also developed a variety of devices for keeping afloat with a minimum of effort. The molluscs, on the other hand, had taken to the bottom and had grown a variety of organs for clinging and crawling there.

The trilobites, primitive relatives of crabs and lobsters, were the most abundant as well as the most notable of these ancient clans. They possessed elaborately differentiated viscera encased in unpalatable shields. Swimming, crawling, and burrowing overlords of their time, they epitomized the gains which the life of that time had won. They were perfectly adjusted for relatively gentle pursuits in relatively quiet water, but they would have been helpless in a sterner environment. They were destined to be equally helpless against the offspring of such an environment.

The formations from which the oldest fossil fishes have been collected, as well as the broken condition of the remains, point clearly to the dynamic water of rivers as their place of birth. But the manner of their birth is completely unknown. No animal as yet unearthed can be convincingly upheld as a very immediate ancestor. No backboneless creature of the sea moves with the side to side undulations of a fish. A weed caught on a boulder in a stream moves in that fashion because it is the only possible compromise a limp object can make with the force of the water and the force of gravity. Chamberlin has suggested that some vagrant wormlike forbear of the fishes may have clung similarly to rocks in streams; that when it needed to alter its position it merely accentuated the movement imparted by the water. But how the nervous system, which is below the digestive tract in the worm, came to occupy a position above it in the fish; how the weak flesh and the external skeleton of the worm gave rise to the muscled flesh and the internal skeleton of the fish, nobody knows.

Though the cause of the evolution of backboned animals is vague, the effect is clear. Backbone revolutionized the living world. By the middle of the Paleozoic era the fishes ruled the oceans as well as the streams, and their descendants were being groomed to rule the lands. The first backboned animals to rise from the sea were doubtless not driven by any great love of adventure. Like their counterparts in the vegetable kingdom, like every other creature that ever brought anything new to the world, they were doubtless driven only by necessity. Under the whip of necessity the fishes had somehow developed new organs of locomotion. Under the whip of necessity their offspring developed not only new organs of locomotion but new organs of respiration as well.

The origin of the earliest four-footed animals, like the origin of most everything else in Nature, is largely a matter for conjecture. The living lungfishes of tropical streams and bayous, however, embody a pregnant clue. When drought destroys their watery homes they house themselves in cocoons with mud cemented by the slime of their bodies. Gulping air into swim bladders which function as primitive lungs, they wait for the rain. When it finally comes the cocoons dissolve, and the lung breathers become gill breathers again.

The immediate ancestors of land vertebrates have not yet been found in the rocks, but their habits, anatomy, and environment were probably not unlike those of living lung-fishes. Drought was frequent during the early middle stages of the Paleozoic era, and the fishes in fresh water sloughs must frequently have been forced to breath air or die. No one can know how many years and lives were consumed before the lungfishes emerged. It is only known that they did emerge before the close of the Devonian period. It is known that at the same time and under the same conditions others emerged whose lungs were so well adapted to air and land that they had virtually ceased to be fishes.

These were the amphibians whose late Paleozoic importance is so shabbily memorialized by the negligible frogs and salamanders of today. Entering the new environment of the land after plants had made it habitable, they began the drive that was destined to extend the mastery of backbone over every environment on earth. The amphibians, however, completed their service with the bridge they had built from the sea. Like the earliest plants of the land they were rooted in the water. The mark of the fish was indelibly stamped upon them. Like fishes they laid their eggs in the water and in youth they breathed like fishes through gills. Even when lungs and legs matured, their skin remained slimy and thirsty. They were a compromise clan and their triumph was part defeat. Others were chosen to carry the colors to higher ground.

The problems of these animals were comparable to the problems of the plants that had preceded them in the conquest of the drier uplands, and they were solved by comparable devices. Fertilization was shifted from the open water to the closed interior of the female, where the sperm might more easily and safely attain its goal. Eggs were toughened with shell against the hot breath of the land, and enlarged to hold food for the embryos within. The young were, accordingly, born relatively mature, air breathers from the beginning. Reptiles were the first animals to gain these benefits. They were the first animals, as cycads were the first plants, that could wander very far from the swamps. And wander they did, reptiles and cycads together, to the ends of the Mesozoic world.

The spectacular success of the early reptiles is a chapter in the story of life that everyone has read. Yet despite the fulness of their famous achievements, two achievements were denied them. No reptile is known to have acquired warm blood with its boon of vigor, or a placenta with its boon of safety. Despite their mimicry of the reptiles in other regards, the mammals gained both these advantages. By doing so they carried forward the banner of vertebrate evolution.

Warm blood was the logical outcome of one major trend in this evolution. Once deprived of the bounty of the sea, the backboned animals had to hustle for a living. The deserts of the late Paleozoic era reduced the supply of food and drink. Oases were fickle and far apart, and only the fleet could prosper. It may well have been under the stimulus of such conditions that the reptilian ancestors of birds and mammals rose off their phlegmatic bellies, and by running raised the temperature of their blood. It may well have been under the stimulus of the glacial cold which followed that their offspring were able to develop most fully the dynamic powers of the backboned body.

The placenta was the logical outcome of another major trend in vertebrate evolution. The reptilian method of reproduction was a vast improvement over that of the fish, but the mammalian method was an equal improvement over the reptilian. For in the mammals the beneficial habit of internal fertilization was retained, and the hazardous habit of egg-laying was practically abandoned. The placenta which fosters and matures most mammals before they are born, and the milk glands which extend the ministrations of the placenta after birth, have made mammals the safest and most efficient reproducers in the world.

Animated by warm blood, protected by the placenta and the mammary glands, mammals have ruled the earth since the start of the Cenozoic era. They stand at one end of a chain whose other end lies in the primordial sea. Nothing in the past suggests that this chain will not continue to lengthen. But what creatures will form the links of the future, and in what direction will they trend?

IV

It is apparent from even so brief a survey of the past that emergent evolution is not a theory but a fact. Both plants and animals have moved with time toward greater efficiency and safety. But it is also apparent that progress has not been indiscriminately vouchsafed to all. Nearly every major stage in the evolution of life is commemorated by contemporary creatures that have obviously failed to progress beyond the stages they commemorate.

The relatively few creatures that did progress paid dearly for the privilege. Every great evolutionary advance began with the ultimatum that creatures either change or die. Running water imposed such an ultimatum on the ancestors of the fishes, drought on the ancestors of the amphibians, aridity on the ancestors of the reptiles, aridity and cold on the ancestors of the mammals. A series of such ultimata changed certain plants from scum on the sea to trees on the land. The lack of such an ultimatum enabled the clam to remain forever a sluggard in the mud.

Every great advance also began with organisms of exceptional plasticity. It was not the rigidly successful trilobite that gave rise to the fish, but some obscure and flexible contemporary. It was not the prosperous sea-going shark that fathered the amphibian, but some poor relation of the sloughs. It was no amphibian of any repute that gave the reptile to the world, no famous family of dinosaurs that flowered in the mammal. It was rather in every case some primitive and plastic creature that had not crystallized in the mold of a special adaptation.

If the past is any prophet of the future the next great evolutionary advance will come to some comparably primitive organism via the toe of some comparably harsh environment. The insects are sufficiently humble and at the same time sufficiently enterprising to be mentioned frequently as likely candidates for this distinction. Though not impressive as individuals, their number and variety are both beyond computation. There is scarcely an organic substance too lean to nourish them. They can perform even the difficult feat of wresting edible compounds of nitrogen and carbon from cellulose. Their presence in the world is a constant threat to the health and welfare of the mammals, including man. What are their chances of becoming the future rulers of the world?

Since the dawn of the modern era in the Eocene epoch some fifty million years ago, insects have shared the world with the mammals. Though the partnership has not been invariably happy, it has never been seriously threatened by revolutionary strife. If the insects had been destined to exterminate the mammals, they would probably have done so long ago. If a new type of evolutionary movement had been destined to start among them, it would probably have started when they were yet undifferentiated and plastic. Insects today are as rigidly specialized as any animals that ever lived. They are as far as possible from the primitive and plastic condition which one would expect to supply the seed of evolutionary innovation.

One would, furthermore, expect any significant advance in the future to extend the dominant line of progress from the past. Such creatures as insects and birds are marvelously adjusted to the lives they lead, but they are dead-end offshoots from the main chain of animal evolution. It is reasonable to expect that the mammals who stand at the end of the chain today might be the ones to extend it tomorrow. But where among the specialized duck-moles, kangaroos, horses, elephants, cats, bats, beavers, whales, and primates is the creature of destiny to be found?

The search for a mammal of sufficient plasticity and promise to qualify as a likely source of something new in the living world must ultimately lead to the last. For the primates alone among mammals exhibit a comparatively primitive stage of adaptation along their peculiar line of specialization. And only man among the primates combines with the primitiveness common to his group a plasticity which is uniquely his own. Though man considers himself the climax of evolution (when he deigns to consider himself a part of it at all), he is one of the most crudely modeled and poorly adapted animals in the world. Indeed, it is partly his lack of finish that commends him as the creature most likely to become in the future what he thinks he already is.

Despite manifest shortcomings, man is the one creature who might conceivably bring a new value into the world. Before his arrival on earth progress was apparently wholly unplanned by the species that progressed. Man himself has advanced to his present status very largely by chance. He was born, it would seem, of tree-dwelling ancestors when the wall of the Himalayas took form across central Asia. Cold and aridity shriveled the trees and forced him to live on the ground.* By fighting the hardships of the new environment he acquired a superior brain, just as unconsciously as the fish under comparable circumstances acquired a superior skeleton. With the ingenuity of this brain, but still without conscious direction, he acquired new food, clothing, weapons, fire, and speech—and through them an unprecedented ability to dominate both his environment and himself. But he has not yet used his powers for his aggregate good.

Self-directed evolution, indeed, is the one great adventure in living that no species has ever tried. Because of the incomparable power of his mind, man is the one species that might possibly try it and succeed. He is clearly such a combination of primitiveness and promise as has mothered all evolutionary advances, and he has been lashed to his present condition by the whip of a harsh environment. Should he ever succeed in directing his own evolution toward some rational and moral goal, man would inaugurate a Psychozoic era which might well be fundamentally different from the eras that have gone before. What are his chances of doing so?

At a time when civilization appears to be headed for the grave the chances of progress may well seem slight. But so might the chances of progress have seemed during all previous evolutionary crises. Danger and hardship are the traditional roads to achievement. There has never been any advance guarantee that danger would not lead merely

* Some anthropologists believe that the ancestors of man merely grew too large to live comfortably in the trees and too intelligent to be content to stay there.

to destruction and hardship merely to death. There can
be no such guarantee now for man. There can only be the
presumption that if security and new life are to come to him
they are likely to come, as they have always come, in the
guise of doom.

Chapter X

IS MAN AN ABSURDITY?

Were it permissible to speak so of Nature, we might call her a sadist with a sense of humor. We might say that she has perpetrated many a cruel joke upon her children. In an age of meticulously unsentimental agnosticism, however, we may only observe that her ways are scarcely those of propriety and compassion.

The evidence of this fact is more easily found than an appropriate idiom to express it. A man need not go to the sea where so many millions of creatures are born for the few that are permitted to survive; nor to the pond where the May fly liberates her eggs only when her body has rotted. He need not even step into the garden where the successful drone must die as he succeeds, and where the unsuccessful ones pay similarly for failure. He need only remain in the house and look at the mirror to see a creature as capriciously devised as any other.

Seeing, however, does not necessarily involve believing. For so quaintly constructed a thing as man, it almost necessarily does not involve believing. When first he saw in the mirror the unmistakable though altered visage of an ape, he howled to heaven that it was not so. Today he is still howling, but not so much in denial of what he sees as in affirmation of what he does not see.

Few modern men are any longer shocked by the compelling evidence of their simian origin and affiliations. Not a few can even be amused by the vulgarities of the monkey house, so similar except in frankness to their own. Those whom these similarities set to thinking may rejoice that above the shoulders men are gods, however bestial they may yet be elsewhere. Or they may reverse the reason for rejoicing.

Were it possible to formulate the average opinion of civilized man on this matter, or even the average opinion of one average man, it would probably disclose a compromise. Man enjoys his ferments and hormones as well as his dreams and aspirations. He is content with being a mongrel blend of god and beast. Indeed, he is more than content. He is proud.

Were he to attempt to examine himself as dispassionately as an entomologist examines a grasshopper, however, he must suspect what a biologically clumsy compromise he is. In the animal pursuits of eating, fighting, and breeding, his prowess hardly matches his customary estimation of it. The tapeworm is easily a better feeder, the weasel a better fighter, the rabbit a better lover. The best human swimmers, runners, and fliers, are inept amateurs when compared with sharks, horses, and hawks. His brain alone saves man from being a wholly generalized and undistinguished animal.

As a god, he is scarcely more effective. Though he is the one creature who can significantly alter himself and his environment to suit his private tastes, he is the only one who is obviously maladjusted with himself and his environment. He is the one creature who might possibly obtain the necessities of life without robbing and killing his fellows, yet he is the most inordinately acquisitive and the most ruthlessly murderous of all. He is the one creature who can know very much about himself and the world, and the only one who is habitually deluded. He is the one creature who can laugh and the only one who is persistently unhappy. He is the one creature who can dodge many harsh and dangerous exactions of Nature only to run

foul of more harsh and dangerous devices of his own manufacture.

One need be no philosopher, pondering in metaphysical
abstractions the problems of human duality, to see that man
might be more a god were he less an animal, and vice versa.
Between these two stools he falls to the ground, not wholly
content to crawl nor wholly able to rise. The pterodactyl
with the teeth of a reptile, the wings of a bird, and the
neck of a mammal, was a somewhat similar hybrid. Without conscious direction the pterodactyl achieved a modicum of success in spite of his incongruities. Will man be
able by conscious direction to succeed as well? Or will he
go down in history as a mere absurdity?

II

Before we can attempt any reasonable answers to these
questions we must know what we mean by success. Most
creatures have little demonstrable capacity for experience
beyond the basic routine of nourishment, defense, and reproduction. Success for them as individuals consists in
eating and avoiding being eaten until reproduction is
achieved. Success for them as species consists in the attainment of a sufficient number of individual successes in
each generation to prevent extinction.

Obviously for man the definition must be enlarged.
Mere survival is not all of success for a creature with a
god in its head. On the other hand, mere survival must be
the first concern of a god who chooses to reside in a beast,
if the strange cohabitation is to continue. Any sound attempt to foretell the future of man must, therefore, start
with an appraisal of his chances for physical survival.

Man was not fashioned in a day, nor did he rise from the
sea of the past a readymade Venus devoid of the marks of

his manufacture. He is the product of a billion years of experimentation, and he shows it. The brine of the sea that gave up his earliest ancestors still flows in his veins. The bones that served his forbears still serve him.

When men evolved the modern motor car, they discarded with each new model such gadgets as had failed to justify their existence. They retained the essential parts, and with each new model improved them. When Nature evolved modern man, she improved only the brain, the larynx, and the hands, and allowed all other essential parts to degenerate. Instead of discarding the non-essential gadgets, she built them into the finished product.

Man, in fact, is an appalling hodge-podge of second hand odds and ends. Last of all creatures to have been turned off the endless belt of evolution, he is first in the number and variety of rusted and outmoded anatomical devices. To study the human physique in detail is to see what old junk has gone into its construction and to marvel that it works as well as it does.

Nature's technique in the manufacture of mankind is epitomized in her technique of manufacturing an individual man. During most of the nine months required to build a baby from an egg, she seems more bent on making a moving picture than a man. The major victories in a billion years of evolution are reënacted in the growing embryo. The egg itself suggests the hypothetical creature that first squirmed out of the primordial muck. Early stages in the cleavage of the egg suggest such primitives of the sea as the coral and the sponge. Later the gill slits of a fish appear, still later the limbs of an amphibian, and eventually the tail of a mammal. Not until birth is imminent does Nature shape the foetus to the semblance of a man.

As an interesting proof of evolution this pageantry is

beyond reproach. As a method of making a man it is, to say the least, rather dilatory and distracted. But it would not be bad if Nature allowed her parade of antiques to pass along, and then began construction with fresh material. Instead, she works her favorite relics into the embryo and into the man who is born of it.

Gill slits are admirable and necessary appurtenances in a fish. They are an essential part of his breathing mechanism. Remodeled in man to become part of his mechanism of hearing, they are at best an awkward makeshift. At worst they revert to their original condition, cleaving the neck of their unfortunate possessor so that fluids taken in at the mouth may leak out at the ear or neck. Similarly, an external tail and a coat of fur are useful and becoming to a dog. They are no detriment to a man so long as they disappear, as they usually do, with birth. But like the gill slits, the tail and fur of the foetus may persist to plague the man.

That the tail has degenerated in man to a usually well hidden bone at the base of the spine is an asset to beauty without being a liability to health. That man normally no longer has sufficient hair to shed water and to retain warmth is of no concern so long as he has a house and a suit of clothes. Nor does it matter that the pineal body— all that is left of the median eye of some distant ancestor— is only a quaint and harmless oddity hidden in the brain. Atrophy of the skin muscles, so useful to man's quadruped kin for flicking off flies and for making faces at menacing neighbors, is effectively counterbalanced by the agility of his hands and the resourcefulness of his head. The only real need for these muscles is in the cinema, and more than enough people retain the use of them to supply the grimacing that Hollywood requires.

The progressive decadence of more essential organs,

however, is a matter of less indifference. Though the safety of modern man does not depend wholly on the perfect functioning of eye and ear, it is fostered not inconsiderably by the ability to tell red from green, and to hear the whistle of a locomotive. Though softened by cooking, his food is more nourishing if his jaws can chew and his intestines churn. Whether the inventor will be able to make artificial machines capable of performing such work, or the physician discover ways to stay the degeneration of the natural machines for doing it, is the future's secret.

As a genus, man has existed for a relatively short period. The million odd years of his geologic history are but a moment when compared with the lengthy day of the trilobite or the pterodactyl. Yet in that moment enough changes were recorded to indicate the present trend of his physical development. On them must be based any respectable speculations concerning his future as an animal.

Scientists are generally agreed that men and apes were derived from a common ancestor. Though in some quarters it is still necessary to emphasize the fact that this hypothetical creature was not technically an ape, many idealistic and even religious people today are able to dispense with the salve of Victorian evasion. They are willing to admit that he was probably not at all like an angel; that should he come in at the door, they would doubtless go out at the window. They can believe that men and apes are cousins under their skins, consoled by the knowledge that with time the relationship has become more distant. Yet they cannot quite escape the feeling that apes are horrible caricatures of themselves. Consequently, they are apt to overlook the fact that not all comparisons of man and ape are to the disadvantage of the ape.

After a million years of reaching for the moon on his

hind legs, man's intestines have sagged and his pelvic girdle has narrowed. Constipation and the agony of childbirth, instead of the moon, came down upon him. After a million years of reaching for nothing more lofty than a mate or a cocoanut, the ape has achieved his ambitions, such as they are, without losing any of his capacity to enjoy them.

Reduction in size and power of muzzle, jaw, and teeth brought a refinement to the face of man which no ape enjoys. It also brought the dentist and the specialist on nose and throat, which not even an ape could enjoy. Perfection of hand and head brought man the exquisite pleasure of reason and imagination—and their exquisite pain. The ape suffers neither from the absence of the one nor the presence of the other.

Nevertheless, neither these nor any of the other possible arguments in favor of the ape could make a sane man want to change places with him. Men love their own anatomy and physiology as they love their own children and automobiles. Two facts, none the less, are clear. Ever since men and apes definitely parted company in the dawn of the Pleistocene period, men have lost not a few of the physical felicities which apes have retained. By the tokens of geologic history, they will probably lose more in the future.

Not one organ of the human body is surely known to be evolving toward increased effectiveness. Man's hands, which next to his brain have been his most valuable asset, are not destined in the future to be the indispensable adjuncts of the mind that they were in the past. Because modern machinery all but manipulates itself, they can only be expected to degenerate with the rest of the human body. The brain itself seems fated to grow no better. Men know vastly more today than the ancients knew, without any demonstrably greater capacity for knowing. There is no reason for believing that this capacity will be any greater tomorrow. Indeed, though learning and possibly wisdom will march ahead, psychoses will probably trail not far behind.

Only too obvious is the error of that romanticism which has seen in evolution an unqualified striving toward perfection and in man the achievement of the goal. It is only too obvious that, physically at least, man is not the triumphant chapter at the close of a saga but a repetitious and poorly constructed paragraph—possibly somewhere in the middle. The only reasonable assumption for the future is a continuance of the degenerative trend in the human physique.

But it is also only reasonable to assume that man will continue to fight degeneration with ingenuity, and with more or less success. Despite the physical deficiencies of men as individuals, man as a species is quite as successful as most other creatures. Through elaborate care of the young and fervid opposition to any curtailment of their production, man is actually the most rapidly increasing animal on earth. Though the weak and the criminal are too largely responsible for this increase to make us regard it with satisfaction, there is at least no threat of extinction for the immediate future. The gravest dangers for man as a species lie less in the crumbling beast than in the bungling god.

III

By a strange perversity in the cosmic plan, the biologically good die young. Species are not destroyed for their shortcomings but for their achievements. The tribes that slumber in the graveyards of the past were not the most simple and undistinguished of their day, but the most complicated and conspicuous. The magnificent sharks of the Devonian period passed with the passing of the period, but certain contemporaneous genera of primitive shellfish are still on earth. Similarly, the lizards of the Mesozoic era have long outlived the dinosaurs who were immeasurably their biologic betters. Illustrations such as these could be endlessly increased. The price of distinction is death.

The reason lies largely in the rigidity with which the progressive species have become adjusted to their particular environments. When man bred certain types of horses for the qualities demanded by the racetrack, he deprived them of other qualities inherent in the nature of horseflesh. The more brilliantly a horse performs on the track the less patiently and surely will it perform in a harness or on a mountain trail. What man has done to the racehorse, Nature has done to innumerable other creatures.

She shapes her darlings for special conditions, and they thrive. Most of them are as automatic in their reactions as adding machines, but they are also as free from self-inspired error. As long as conditions are constant, they lead safe and easy lives. But Nature is notoriously fickle. She changes the conditions without any warning or reason. Her erstwhile darlings, too set in their anatomy and their ways to meet the new demands, must die.

Man is one of Nature's darlings, but a darling with a difference. In possessing an organ which is at once his greatest strength and his greatest weakness, he is not unlike the others. When Nature gave him his brain and with it the unprecedented privilege of contributing to the arrangement of his own life, she included the less enviable capacity of suffering for his own mistakes. By thus being endangered through the flexibility rather than the rigidity of his specialized organ, he is unique.

The human brain, like the feet of an antelope or the claws of a cat, is the outstanding attribute of its owner. Unlike the feet of an antelope or the claws of a cat, it has widened rather than restricted the field of its owner's activities. Without it man would still be chattering in a Paradise of bananas. With it he has wandered away from the trees to discover weapons, clothing, fire, coöperative living, articulate speech, abstract thought, and countless attendant diversities of experience. Without it he would never have forsaken the shelter of the forest for the hazards of a wider world. With it he not only accepted the hazards already in this world, but he added others of his own invention.

Though man has reached his present position without greatly taxing his power of conscious self-direction, he has obviously passed the turning point of his career. During the more or less civilized last five thousand years, he has increasingly contributed to the arrangement of his own life. This period is scarcely half of one percent of his sojourn on earth, but it limns the probable pattern of his future evolution.

It shows that the significant changes of the future are apt to come through his mind and spirit, and consequently very largely through his own direction. Through them he can bring happiness and misery upon himself, conditions which for him as a god are equivalent to success and failure. Is it likely that the tackle of civilization will fish up more happiness than misery from the unplumbed deeps of mind and spirit, so that ultimately man may triumph as a god though he fail as a beast? The answer that history returns is simple enough. Unless he change both his tackle and his tactics, no.

To be born, to eat, to reproduce, and to die, is the most that most creatures can wrest from the world. But they easily accept the narrowness of their lives through the simple device of not being aware of it. Man alone possesses a mechanism of discovery and discontent. Curiosity about himself and the world, and distaste for what his curiosity reveals, are two of his most dominant and distinctive traits. Disguising and altering distasteful conditions have been two of his most dominant and distinctive activities.

Long before the last great ice sheet had begun to recede from the face of Europe some twenty-five thousand years ago, man had already become unique in the animal kingdom. Though far more apelike than any of his living descendants, he already could do what no other creature had ever done before. He could not only strike fire, make tools, and wield weapons with his hands, but he could also dream dreams with his head.

Where the skeletons of these Neandertal men have been found in their original burial grounds, they were accompanied by implements and the remains of food. The only possible interpretation of such facts is that man had already fallen in love with himself; that he had already begun to hope, perhaps even to believe, that death does not kill all; that, in short, the temporal limitations of existence had already grown intolerable to him.

They have been intolerable ever since. Men still hope, when they cannot believe, that for the spirit at least death does not exist. But while they dream of an endless eon of bliss beyond the grave, on this side they go on living in the flesh, briefly like other animals. Unfortunately they are not godlike enough to be wholly content with their dreams of an everlasting future, nor bestial enough to be wholly undisturbed by the facts of a fleeting present.

They go on, however, with their dreaming and pretending, dressing up the baseness as well as the briefness of their lives. For each crude exigency of survival they invent a noble motive and a pleasing manner. They are the only creatures who are both moral and polite. Beneath the veneer of evasions, however, is the ancient lust and pain and cruelty of living. And, unhappily, they know it.

Man will doubtless never achieve perfection in self-deception, but he will doubtless continue to try. The fundamentals of existence must continue to shock his sensibilities, and he must continue to protect himself howsoever he may. Though hypocrisy helps him only a little in this endeavor, he prizes it (as he should) for that little. But he will probably never let it replace the other major division of human activity which is concerned rather with changing than with disguising distasteful things.

Most creatures take the world as they find it. They instinctively become partners with their environment. They make working agreements even with such inhospitable places as deserts, hot springs, and subterranean pools of oil. And only rarely in using their surroundings do they abuse them.

Man, on the contrary, is not willing to take the world as he finds it. Only rarely does he use his surroundings without abusing them, and without eventually abusing himself. In countless ways he stupidly exploits his environment for immediate gain at the expense of ultimate loss.

He harnesses the rivers for a thousand tasks and repays them in pollution. He builds smelters whose breath, like that of Rappaccini's daughter, is deadly to all it touches. He builds levees to control floods and at the same time destroys the forests without which there can be no effective control. By overgrazing and overplowing, he turns grasslands into deserts where not even sheep can graze nor food plants grow. By transplanting such creatures as the English sparrow and the rabbit, he enables them in the end to become more pestiferous than the pests they were employed to subdue. The net result of such achievements is an increasing unbalance of man and his external environment. Though his genius for maladjustment may never seriously threaten his existence as a species, it considerably weakens his standing as a god.

Internally, his condition is more serious. To be sure, by tampering with himself he has smoothed many stretches on the road from the cradle to the grave. Through medicine he has made himself a little sounder, through plumbing a little cleaner, through education and art a little wiser and finer, through all perhaps a little happier. But he has also made himself immensely complex and confused. He is mentally and spiritually muscle-bound. He stands like Tantalus in the midst of his blessings, unable to assemble them for his own greatest good.

Man is easily the most elaborately organized of all the gregarious and social animals. His society has grown increasingly intricate with the growth of civilization. Yet where today is the human state that operates as effectively as a beehive? Where is the family as stable and contented as a gorilla and his wives? Even though the answer be "nowhere," man neither envies nor aspires to emulate the bee or the gorilla. Through this attitude he molds his most embarrassing dilemma. The crude simplicity of animals offends him, so he embroiders their simplicity (which is also fundamentally his own) until he is tripped and tied by the strands of the embroidery.

By a strange combination of generosity and greed he protects the weak in asylums and kills the strong in futile wars. By a strange combination of idealism and eroticism he seeks without finding a satisfactory system of intersexual relationships. By a strange combination of ingenuity and impotence, he multiplies the basic necessities of life far beyond any possible need, only to let millions go hungry and unclothed for lack of a rational and equitable distribution.

Man can plumb the immensity of interstellar space and probe the minuteness of the atom. He can invent ingenious devices for his own comfort and entertainment. He can make pictures and music more sublime than any sight or sound in Nature, and poetry more beautiful and just than any she ever conceived. But he has not yet achieved through all these special powers the peace, tranquillity, and general well-being in the world that oysters possess without them.

IV

In view of all this, is not man as a species an absurdity, a hodge-podge of characteristics that will not work together for the good of the whole? In view of all this, he may well be; but, fortunately, all this is not all. His very confusion suggests less that he has definitely failed than that he has not yet taken definite form. He may be the grub of a butterfly to come.

Compared with many another species, man is very young. Though the evolution of his body has probably stopped, the evolution of his mind and spirit may have just begun. The waste and confusion of the past may have been only the bustle of a clumsy start. Nature has always been an inefficient wastrel, and man, though unique, is yet her child.

As a species, man can never excel the average of the parts, and the average is still a grub in mind and spirit. Yet individuals of exceptional and varied qualities—scientists, educators, administrators, artists, and saints—are continually appearing. They do for the mental and spiritual evolution of man what mutations do for the physical evolution of other creatures. They tend to combat a rigid standardization of type. Though Caesars and Napoleons will doubtless continue to rise from time to time, and freeze whole

nations with fear or greed or desperation, they are ultimately self-defeating. The violence of their actions breeds
violent reactions, and the species continues to flux. As long
as there is flux there is danger, but there is also hope.

The problem of the future is to discover how the sporadic
strength of individual men may be extended to embrace
mankind. The need of the future is more knowledge of
man, both as an individual and as a species. The folly and
heartbreak of prescribing for him without such knowledge has been only too freshly and too clearly shown.

It is odd that the nature of stars and the behavior of
gases should have stimulated far more and far abler inquiry
than have the nature and behavior of men. To be sure, they
are more gratifying subjects for study because they are
more simple. But man can live without knowledge of stars
and gases, whereas he is finding it increasingly difficult to
live without knowledge of himself. Without such knowledge he is finding it increasingly difficult to benefit from
his vast and growing knowledge of everything else.

Dr. Carrel of the Rockefeller Institute has brought to
general attention in a recent book man's appalling ignorance of himself. Dr. Hooton of Harvard has recently outlined a plan which might help repair the deficiency. It is
simply a proposal for an institute of clinical anthropology
where the present status of man as a species might be as-
certained, and where guiding principles for the future
might just possibly be discovered.

Because the problems of man as a species have never appeared very important to men in their selfish pursuits as
individuals, anthropologists and philosophers have been
lonely and few. Physicians and priests, though many, have
been concerned with the plight of the individual. Innumerable institutions exist whose purpose is human better-
ment, but it would seem that not one is devoted to a broad

understanding of the creature it is attempting to improve. Such an institution would be a help without being a panacea. Only fools and charlatans have panaceas for the varied distempers of humanity. When Nature vouchsafed that man might assist at the shaping of his own fate, she withheld many automatic safeguards against error which she freely bestowed upon other creatures. No other creature has ever faced sterner problems with fewer guides to workable solutions. Analysis of this strange embarrassment, to be sure, will not yield specific remedies for relieving it. But it will reveal the basis on which a sound science of man must rest.

Chapter XI

THE EMBARRASSMENT OF BEING DIFFERENT

WHEN a squirrel gathers nuts against winter, he is not known to philosophize about them. He does not range them from light to heavy, pondering the reasons for their variation in weight. He does not divide them into rough and smooth, despising the ugliness of the one and delighting in the beauty of the other. He does not classify them as small and large, judging the small ones bad and the large ones good. He does not regard them as proof of his superiority over creatures who do not gather nuts. He merely eats them when the need arises.

When man gathers facts against the cold indifference of Nature, he is not content with their concrete value alone. He searches them for their abstract significance. He judges them for their aesthetic and moral worth. Generally he uses them and frequently he abuses them in the interest of his self-conceit. For man is the only animal who is proud of himself and contemptuous of his kin. He has no quarrel with evolution so long as it is presumed to have been a struggle toward perfection which culminated in his arrival.

Men, who are the most complicated creatures on earth, find it easy to assume that the merit of an animal depends wholly on the degree of its complexity. They look with disdain at lobsters who can build neither aeroplanes nor poems. So, too, by similar tokens might lobsters view clams and clams the lowly worms. Only the amoeba has no one to disdain, but fortunately he does not care.

Even biologists, who are supposed to be impartial, mix

science and snobbery when they call the simpler organisms "lower" and the more elaborate ones "higher."
Though it is true that progress has been marked by a general increase in the complexity of living creatures, it is not
true that the relatively complex organisms have been invariably more successful than the relatively simple. History is strewn with the remains of elaborate anatomical
errors. In the economy of Nature the excellence of an
organism is not measured by the embellishments of anatomy
but by the effectiveness with which it lives.

In water a fox is a lower animal than a fish. On land the
status is reversed. Judged fairly in their own environments,
they are equal. In their own special sphere of living even
the one-celled amoebae are supreme. They lack the size and
strength and motility of the so-called higher animals, yet
in the vastness of their numbers and in their general ability to weather the storms of the world they inhabit they
have proved themselves a biologic success. Others may
claim a different success but not a greater one.

Man's policy of interpreting the facts of biology so that
he invariably comes out on top is not always innocently
academic. The same technique whereby man belittles the
animals is used by men to belittle one another. Granting
the validity of the technique, the conclusions may be reasonable enough. If it is true that Nature had experimented
for a billion years to achieve perfection in the person of
man, it is unlikely that she would stop with the creation
of the first crude human species.

Geological history, indeed, reveals that she did not stop.
The earliest men of Java and China were scarcely more
human than apes. The earliest Piltdown Englishmen and
Heidelberg Germans were but slightly more human than
their Oriental confrères. The later Neandertalers were
indubitably men but they were also indubitably louts. Not

until modern men appeared some twenty-five thousand years ago was manhood—in the opinion of modern men—achieved.

Since then Nature has not evolved any additional species of men. All of the seventeen billion human beings alive today are sufficiently similar to be classed in a single species. Yet it is not likely that Nature would consider the entire species an embodiment of her dream of perfection. It is more likely that she would continue to work toward that noble end by selecting and cementing the superior individuals within it. Despite their similarities, living men are divided by differences in culture, language, and physique. Is it not reasonable to assume that these differences represent an evolutionary sequence? Is it not reasonable to assume that the sequence culminates in the white men who dominate the modern world, and especially in that nation of white men that possesses the strongest army? Many white men and their dictators would quickly say yes.

Most honest anthropologists, however, say no. Simple and sublime though it is, they are not captivated by the conceit that Nature has consciously struggled to elevate mankind. Though many of them are white men, they do not see a clear case for the biological superiority of white men. They do not surely know what constitutes racial superiority. They do not even agree on what constitutes a race.

There is no evidence that evolution has gathered modern men into groups which are genetically or even culturally distinct. Lines of color are the popularly accepted boundaries of race, yet both sex and civilization are continually breaking through them. There is no evidence that evolution has gathered modern men into groups which are genetically or even culturally distinct. Lines of color are the popularly accepted boundaries of race, yet both sex and civilization are continually breaking through them. There is no evidence that evolution has ever blocked out a species on the basis of color. There is no evidence that it is blocking out sub-species of men on that basis.

White men, for example, are anatomically no further from apes than black men are. His high nose and small face make the white man the most human of men; his thin lips and hairiness make him the most apelike. The flat nose and large face of the negro suggest the ape, but no ape has the negro's full red lips and kinky hair. The anatomy of all men, regardless of color, is a blend of simian and human traits.

The brain of a white woman is apt to be slightly smaller than the brain of her similarly pigmented husband, but slightly larger than the brain of her negro maid. It does not follow, however, that the mental excellence of the three must hold to similar proportions. Davenport and Steggerda concluded from their study of Jamaican blacks and whites that the blacks were superior in musical ability and the whites in matters of judgment. But obviously there is no way to determine which of these *aptitudes* is superior, because there is no unprejudiced basis whereon the two may be compared. Similarly impossible of proof is the traditional assumption of the male that he is more intelligent than his wife. Though her brain may be somewhat smaller and her faculties different, she is not necessarily inferior. Men themselves have been known to concede that the brains of other men's wives are superior to those of their husbands.

If size of brain alone were an accurate measure of intelligence, elephants would be twice as intelligent as men. If size of brain in proportion to weight of body were an accurate measure of intelligence, humming birds would be more intelligent than men, Eskimos would be more intelligent than whites, and Neolithic man would have been the most intelligent human that ever lived.

Within the relatively short range of variability in the brains of normal living men, there is no demonstrable correlation of size and function. Many criminals, for example, have larger brains than the general average; many geniuses have smaller. To grade the brains of men as one grades eggs is to assume that the human brain is as simple as an egg. Possibly the brain that assumes so is.

The structure of the brain is a somewhat better index of mentality than its size. The brain of an elephant is much larger but also much less developed than the brain of a man, which possibly accounts for the different mentalities of elephants and men. Among men, however, the structural differences in the brain though many are very slight. They cannot yet be surely correlated with differences in mental ability. In short, the intelligence of a normal individual cannot be definitely gauged either by the size or the structure of his brain. It is therefore absurd to evaluate the intellectual status of a race with its multitude of individuals on that basis.

Though the white man's brain is not demonstrably better than the brains of other men, it is demonstrably producing more spectacular results. White men mine more minerals, manufacture more machinery, build more cities, sail more ships, run more governments, enjoy a greater variety of pleasures, and think a greater variety of thoughts than all the rest of humanity combined. No one may deny their cultural ascendancy today. Yet history attests that long before Nordic self-love and attainment had risen out of barbarism, red men were once comparably ascendant in Peru, and yellow men in China.

It is impossible to prove that biologic superiority is the foundation on which such civilizations have been erected.

Both the physical and the cultural peculiarities of men have mingled endlessly in the surge of warring and migrating peoples. An infinity of forces both social and biologic have kept humanity in constant flux. Men gather in groups like kelp beds in the sea, and then separate and reassemble in differently constituted groups. The tide that favors one group today will favor another tomorrow.

No bonds have ever been able to keep any particular assemblage of human qualities indefinitely intact. To define a race in terms of such fortuitous and fluid values as langauge, culture, or nationality, is absurd. To define it in terms of color is even more absurd. Skin pigment is a waste product of metabolism, and racial distinctions based on it are a waste product of the mind. The amount of pigment in the skin of a man is no more significant than the amount of hair on his pate.

Neither the culture nor the physique of any race, however defined, or of any subdivision of any race, is pure. Isolation and inbreeding develop such extreme types as the Eskimo and the jungle Negro, but even these do not stand wholly apart from the rest of mankind. Their traits like the traits of other peoples were drawn very largely from a common humanity. Racial purity is biologically non-existent and impossible though the hokum and hate which sustain a belief in it are real enough.

II

The mingling of traits in individual men is comparable to their mingling in the species. Though the attributes of humanity tend to gather into recognizably different individual assemblages, there is no purity or solidity in the grouping. Some men become soldiers, for example, and others saints; some thinkers and others doers. Figs do not spring from thistles, but soldiers and men of action have fathered saints and men of thought. There is no respectable biologic explanation for the differences between such types of men. There are not even any precise definitions of the types. Soldiers sometimes have peaceful impulses and saints occasionally sin. Men of thought have been known to act and men of action to think.

It is ridiculous to consider any type of human being as a definite block in an inflexible mosaic. It is ridiculous to judge one type superior to another. From the point of view of efficiency, all types are superior in their own special fields of activity and inferior in all other fields. Measured by efficiency alone Sir Basil Zaharoff who worked for the misery and slaughter of his fellows was the equal of Louis Pasteur who worked for their happiness and health.

By the shifting standards of conventional morality any type may be superior today and inferior tomorrow, as, for example, the pacifist who is a patriot in peacetime but a traitor in war. By such conflicting standards as honesty and manners, any type may in fact be both superior and inferior at the same time. A statesman may be superior in the honesty of his opinions but inferior in the manner of expressing them. And also, alas, *vice versa*.

Just as each type of humanity may be differently appraised by different standards, so may each of a multitude of human traits. The quality of aggressiveness, for example, might be superior and its reverse inferior when judged by the ideals of a capitalistic state. The opposite might be true in a state where the profit motive did not exist. Almost any human quality, indeed, might be superior by one standard and inferior by another. Even feeblemindedness, generally judged inferior, is by one measure superior. "In a world which has much low-grade work to be done," says a recent report of the American Neurological Association, "there is still room for the people of low-grade mentality of good character."

In such a welter of conflicting and shifting values, where is the Good that reformers seek? Where is the Humanity to which they would make it apply? May any of the traits, pursuits, or conditions of men be considered in general either good or bad? If so, what standard shall be used to prove them so and how may the standard in its turn be proved either good or bad?

History attests that these questions are not idle nor their answers easy. It all too amply shows the futility of applying to the intricate and fluxing problems of mankind the simple and static formulae that men adore. Both as an individual and as a species man is complex and confused. He is the only creature that is chronically at odds with itself and its environment because he is the only creature that is consciously and continuously altering itself and its environment.

Must we conclude from this that man has been doomed to flux forever but never to evolve? Must we conclude that he is exempt from the fundamental laws that govern other creatures? All other species have ultimately come to rest—either in some uniform and relatively stable adjustment for life, or in death. Man has come to rest in neither. He is at once the most rapidly increasing species on earth and the one most variously and variably adjusted to the life it leads.

It is a truism of biology that man became man when the nervous system of his ancestral stock had reached a certain stage of growth and refinement. From the purely biologic point of view the human nervous system is only a more elaborate model of an older machine. Like every other part of the human body, it is the product of eons of experimentation. No animal could ever have existed without

some means of coördination with the world it had to exploit. No animal could ever have existed without some
means of distinguishing what was good for it from what
was not, some capacity for embracing the one and rejecting
the other. Out of the acorn of these traits in the simpler
animals grew the oak of the brain in the more complex.

Before the invention of nerves, the unembellished flesh
must have reacted directly to the environment. An amoeba
bumping its unicellular way through a watery world,
withdrawing from danger and advancing toward safety,
discriminating between genuine foods and deceptive frauds,
is a brainless little blob of living jelly. Yet in him are the
rudiments of abilities that grace his nobler contemporaries,
just as presumably the germs of special organs for preserving and enhancing these abilities were in his counterparts
of a bygone day.

At first these organs were probably simple muscle tissues, stimulated like those of a living sponge without the
help of nerves. Later, perhaps as in a living coral, a surface network of nerve fibers transmitted sensations from
the outside to the inside of the body. When eventually
creatures were born with a head to explore and a tail to
follow, the nerves were bunched at the investigative end.
The Pre-Cambrian worm with a knot of nerves to the fore
and strings of nervous tissue trailing aft was a pattern for
all the more elaborate animals of the future. Half a billion years of refinement lie between that worm and man,
yet the two are but different models of the same machine.

With the advent of the fish, the evolution of the central
nervous system is illustrated by actual fossils dug from the
rocks. Though much simpler than the brain of a modern
man, the brain of a primitive fish was built along similar
lines. Because sight and hearing are indispensable to the
welfare of a fish, the parts of the brain that control these

senses increased in size as with time more effective fishes were produced. In those offspring of fishes which took to the land, other parts of the brain improved. To be able to smell an enemy and to respond locomotively to the promptings of discretion are vital necessities of life on land. The olfactory lobe and the cerebellum of primitive reptiles were accordingly enlarged to further these ends. At last, when mentality became the ultimate measure of success among mammals, the cerebrum which housed it grew gradually larger and more complex until in men it dwarfed all other parts.

These facts establish beyond reasonable doubt the slow and logical development of the brain from a simple to a complex organ. Yet the striking differences between the behavior of man and that of even his closest relatives are not merely differences of degree. There must have been a time in the gradual evolution of the brain when wholly new functions suddenly and illogically appeared.

Many species before man developed qualities that made them unusual. But wherever there is a good record of their ancestry, the functions as well as the organs of each would seem to have evolved consistently down the avenues of their specialization. The same is true to a large extent of the contemporaries of man. It appears natural that a deer should browse on vegetation, that a wolf should browse on the deer, and that a tapeworm should browse on the wolf. It is inconceivable that a frog should fly like a swallow, or that an elephant should hop like a frog. The individual behavior of each one of these is invariably consistent with its racial history and physique.

The functioning of most organs in the human body is comparably consistent. It is a foregone conclusion that the healthy intestine will digest its food and not itself. It is a foregone conclusion that the heart will pump blood and the lungs air even when their owners are asleep. The behavior of such organs is as automatic and limited as the behavior of a moth or a mouse.

How, on the other hand, may one know what is normal in the behavior of the human mind? There are no precedents for its most important functions, no automatic controls. Suddenly as time is measured by the clock of geology, strange qualities popped into the head of a certain simian species. They are consistent with nothing else in Nature, not even alas with themselves. They have led man away from the stable and stereotyped adjustments of other creatures into a shifty and multiform confusion.

III

The eminent scholars who convened for the celebration of the Harvard Tercentenary believed that if man is ever to be built into an efficiently adjusted species, men themselves must plan the building. They believed that the future welfare of civilization depends upon the ability of civilized men to understand and predict their own behavior, and to control it for their own aggregate good. So they brought their heads together in a symposium on "Factors Determining Human Behavior"—to appraise, as it were, the assets of humanity for the business of directing its own evolution.

The tone of this conference was strange to ears that were ringing with the cant of contemporary politics. The men who were best equipped to find The Answers had obviously not yet found them. Professor Adrian, whose voice is authority in the realm of neurophysiology, could only say that his science might be hoped to improve some of the old methods of control over human behavior but not to contribute any new ones. Dr. Jung spoke of the tremendous intricacy of psychic phenomenology, and of the worthlessness of any attempt to formulate a comprehensive theory of it. Dr. Janet offered some hope of an improved psychotherapeutic technique for helping men who are clinically diseased, but he said nothing about any technique for helping men who are not. Dr. Carnap lauded logic as a help in the diagnosis but not in the cure of intellectual confusion. The cure, he said, must be discovered by psychology and the social sciences. Dr. Malinowski, speaking as a social anthropologist, mentioned no prospect of such a discovery. He closed the symposium with remarks on the backwardness of social science and the impotence of social engineering.

A companion symposium, which dealt with "Authority and the Individual," was not only vague but contradictory. Opinions ranged from conservative to liberal in keeping with the temperament and the point of view of the speakers. These opinions though personal were not the pat little beliefs of smug little minds. They reflected the ablest thought of the ablest minds, and therein lay the tragedy of their antagonisms. For the only conclusion an unbiased listener could possibly have reached after considering them all was that no method that man has yet devised for governing himself is surely either feasible or just.

By analyzing a typically human adaptation we may see something of the reason for man's unprecedented dilemma. Take, for example, the adaptation to fire. Countless creatures before man must have seen lightning kindle a tree, but they reacted chiefly with their feet. Only man reacted to the spectacle of fire with his hands. Like the wool of the woolly rhinoceros the adaptation to fire seems to have originated as a response to the Pleistocene cold of Asia. But the one response was through the skin and the other through ingenuity. The one began in the germ plasm of a few individuals, and the other in the brain. The one was extended to the species by blood and the other by education. The one, in short, was a physical and the other a mental adaptation.

Human adaptations are predominantly mental though they assume a host of physical forms. As such they are different from the predominantly physical adaptations of other creatures. In one regard alone are the two essentially the same. Both are rooted in a capacity for variation. The discoveries and inventions which take shape in the brain cells and the gene combinations which take shape in the germ cells are but different manifestations of the same creative power. Both originate in ways that are dark. Both resist the attempt of science to control them at their source. It is not in their origin but in their survival that the mental variations differ profoundly from the physical.

There is no indication that horses were ever concerned about the proper control of equine behavior, yet equine behavior has always been properly controlled. Physical variation happened to give the ancestors of horses a crude equipment for grazing and running, which happened to be admirably suited to the grassy uplands where most of them lived. Under such circumstances any horse that attempted to fly and eat insects would have been a mistake. Nature did not coddle mistakes in the form of horses. She killed them. She weeded out all variations that strayed into futility. Ruthless with individuals but kind to the race she thinned out the horses for a narrow but effective life.

She has been less strict with men and less solicitous for mankind. Non-physical variations rise like weeds in the social evolution of humanity, a motley horde of discoveries, inventions, religions, governments, economies, and moral codes. Like physical variations they struggle to survive, and many of them fall in the struggle. But they do not fall through failure to meet an inexorable standard of survival. It is not predetermined that any of them shall either stand or fall, or that having once stood or fallen they shall so remain. It is not predetermined that any of them shall decisively make or break the species.

The adaptation of slavery, for example, tacks with the veering winds of history. It is neither permanently established in human society nor permanently debarred. Most human adaptations are like that. They come and go with the moods of the human spirit. They are not selected by natural laws for the lasting welfare of the species but by whims for the temporary advantage of part of it. Because there is no precedent in Nature for these whims, no automatic devices in man to control them for the good of the species as a whole, they have kept the species biologically and socially in chronic flux and confusion.

IV

When Walt Whitman thought he could live with the animals because they do not sweat and whine about their condition he was being particularly human. He was displaying his capacity for discontent, a talent unique in man. By being discontented with his own discontent he was displaying the talent in its loftiest form.

Discontent is the one attribute of man that makes his inconsistent whims consistent, that underlies his peculiar restlessness, that best explains the peculiar confusion of his evolution. Paradoxically, it is also the one quality that best explains the progressive elements of that evolution. It is the one quality that might possibly organize the other qualities for further progress. It has already taken man out of the trees and it may yet take him out of confusion.

For possibly a billion years innumerable species had lived

and died without knowing the fermentation of this strange emotion. Not one had been dissatisfied, not one respectable or unhappy over the whole earth. For possibly a billion years their societies were never disturbed by unrest because the dictatorship of Nature was supreme.

The biologist speaks of the endless variety of creatures today, the paleontologist of their endless variation in the past. But they seldom speak of an inner drive as the likely cause of any of these differences and changes. Geologists widely assume that man became man very largely through the stimulation of the Pleistocene glacial climate. Yet many other creatures who were similarly stimulated ultimately came to rest in well adjusted species. Man alone continued to be stimulated after the climatic stimulus was removed.

No external pressure can wholly explain why the ancestors of man came down from the trees and why the ancestors of gibbons did not. No external pressure can wholly explain why the groundling descendants of these did not stay in the forests with their groundling cousins the gorillas. No external pressure can wholly explain why the later evolution of human culture did not stop at the Piltdown, the Heidelberg, or the Neandertal stages. No external pressure can wholly explain why the one species of man which has existed for 25,000 years or more is still unadjusted and in flux after all those years. Only some inner ferment of unprecedented potency can explain such unprecedented behavior.

When a biologist names a species, he seeks the word which seems best to characterize that species. *Sapiens*, "wise," was selected for the species that includes all modern men. It is a noble word and it was doubtless applied in a noble spirit. By suggesting the ultimate in human knowledge, discernment, and judgment, it describes the nature of man at its best. But it does not even suggest it at its most typical. Nothing so elegant and static as wisdom could have driven the ancestors of modern men from the trees and later from the caves. Nothing so elegant and static could beget the perversities and dilemmas of humanity today. Some cruder and lustier quality must be responsible for that.

We have called this quality discontent. Under a more technical term it would still be the reverse of placid resignation. Through it humanity—alone in the living world—has grown chronically addicted to revolt.

Revolutions of one sort or another have ruffled the history of man from the beginning. Most of them were local readjustments in society, and as such were only breezes on the skirt of the storm. For the history of man as a species has been a revolution. It has been a revolution against a violent and indifferent world, against the colossal waste and hardship of living and dying by the dictates of such a world. Insofar as the hectic affairs of men have possessed any special significance in the past, they have been phases of this revolution. It is the one revolution that makes all others seem trifling and vain.

Men for a million years have revolted against the tyrannies of the physical world. Through an unparalleled aptitude for invention, they have tricked the wind into the sails of their ships, the lightning into their lamps. They have wrested homes from the forest, food from the ground, power from the water, and support from the air. Through an unparalleled aptitude for imitation and education other men have inherited the fruits of these victories. Despite many a blunder in handling his affairs with the outer world, man has become the safest and most comfortable species on earth.

He has become the least safe and comfortable species in regard to the inner world of his own society because he has neglected the larger problems of that world. Knowledge of man has grown in sealed compartments. It is vast but uncoördinated. Little of it applies to a man as the composite of all his attributes, or to mankind as the composite of all men. Revolt against social maladjustments is equally uncoordinated. It typically seeks such good as is local, immediate, and obvious, and disdains or opposes all other kinds of good. If human society is ever to evolve towards some satisfactory internal adjustment, it will do so because men have broadened both their knowledge of themselves and their concept of self-interest; because the general welfare of the human species has become the standard to which all other standards are referred.

Where in the learning or virtue of contemporary men may the means to this end be sought? In their present condition of knowledge and grace a great many men would brand as fantastic the hope that Nature in the form of human nature might ever be altered. Geologic history, however, does not justify their cynicism. It shows that though Nature is reactionary, contentious, and cruel, she is also progressive, coöperative and kind. It shows that human nature is Nature plus the power of conscious choice. It shows that man to a large extent has made himself and his world, and to a large extent can change them.

Minorities of men have already demonstrated—in laboratories, hospitals, churches, and schools—a capacity for extending the welfare of men as individuals. Should majorities of men intelligently and sincerely attempt to extend the welfare of man as a species, who can say what dreams might not possibly come true? It is not for the historian of life to say. Self-directed evolution, so far as he knows, is an adventure without precedent in a billion years.